TIME & TIDE

Stories and Poems from
Solstice Shorts Festival
2019

ARACHNE PRESS

First published in UK 2019 by Arachne Press Limited
100 Grierson Road, London SE23 1NX
www.arachnepress.com
© Arachne Press 2020
ISBNs
Print 978-1-909208-84-1
ePub 978-1-909208-85-8
Mobi/kindle 978-1-909208-86-5
Thanks to Muireann Grealy for her proofing.
Printed on wood-free paper in the UK by TJ International, Padstow.

TIME & TIDE

Contents

Stories

Metharme	CB Droege	10
Listen, Noah's Wife	Roppotucha Greenberg	13
The Fisherman's Wife	Linda McMullen	14
Ballast	Diana Powell	16
The Surgeon's Mate	Maria Kyle	21
A Madras Crossing	Elizabeth Hopkinson	26
Man Overboard	Emily Bullock	29
Remittance	Kilmeny MacMichael	34
Fisherfolk	Juliet Humphreys	39
Diaspora	Neil Lawrence	42
Sea Change	Diana Powell	47
Casting the Stones	Cathy Lennon	52
Herr Dressler	Eoghan Hughes	55
Hingland	Pauline Walker	57
The Dowager Duchess of Berwick-upon-Tweed May or May Not be Bottling It	Rob Walton	62
The Wreck of the Kyllikki	Cindy George	64
The Professor's Daughter	Barbara Renel	67
Granmama's Paradise	Holland Magee	70
The Answer My Friend...	Paul Foy	74
Turquoise	Sheila Lockhart	77

Time Poems

Arrival	Valerie Bence	82
In the Shadows, on the Shore, Leith	Jane Aldous	84
Of Gráinne Ni Mháile	Thomas Tyrrell	86
A Conjuring Poem	Simon Whitfield	88
False Light	John Richardson	89
Church Mary Sounds the Sea	Jenny Mitchell	90
Napoleon	Nick Westerman	92
Clearance	Christine Ritchie	93
How Women Came to Tristan da Cunha	Claire Booker	94
The Sinking of Mrs Margaret Brown	Michelle Penn	95
The Fisherman's Daughter	Claire Booker	96

When You Regret Wishing for Something Thrilling	Emma Lee	97
The nth Wave	Math Jones	98
Frocks of Passage	Mandy Macdonald	100
Overlord with Declan	Elizabeth Parker	102
Sisterhood of the Seas	Alison Lock	105
Half a Dozen Oranges	Mandy Macdonald	106

Tide Poems

The Arctic Diaries	Melissa Davies	108
The Lookout Men	Melissa Davies	108
Halibut	Melissa Davies	109
Værøy	Melissa Davies	110
Seaweed	Melissa Davies	112
Bird Wife	Melissa Davies	112
Verticals	Kate Foley	113
The Watchers	Elizabeth Parker	114
Mother Fish	Ian Macartney	116
Woman from North India on Bostadh Beach	Elinor Brooks	117
Points of Interest	Olivia Dawson	118
We Dig the Pig	Angel Warwick	119
Ovčice, Croatia	Ian Macartney	120
When Will We See the Sea?	Joy Howard	121
I Nearly Drownded, Daddy	Vivien Jones	122
On a Day Like This	Savanna J A Evans	123
Delivery	Holly Blades	124
First Light	Laura Potts	126
Casting a Daughter Adrift	Emma Lee	127
Hawser	Sarah Tait	128
Bosun's Locker	Sarah Tait	129
No Tearaways	Ivonne Piper	130
Sea Lessons	Ness Owen	131
City of Water	JN nucifera	132
Crossing the Black Water	Reshma Ruia	134
Tulpaner och Liljekonvaljer	Carl Alexandersson	136
Paddling	Lynn White	138

Tide Film Texts

Open Water	Susan Cartwright-Smith	140
Modality	Julie Laing	142

STORIES

Metharme
CB Droege

I stand at the prow of the ship, one more in a long, long line of ships. I'm watching the stars, listening to my daughters, thinking of home. Days tend to run together out on the sea. Then the months run together. Then the years. Then the decades, the centuries. Without age, without change, everything runs together. The boats change little, and still seem very similar to the boats of my girlhood. Yes, they have electronic fish finders, computerised maps, and satellite phones, but in the end, they're still just a small group of (mostly) men in a floating machine, trying to get as much fish as possible in as short a time as they can. They compete with other ships; they sing ribald songs; they get in fights; they miss their families; and, sometimes, they drown. So it was three millennia ago, so it is now.

I think of my mother. Her ivory skin, and cold hands. There is so much of her in me. My beauty, my immortality, both come from her. It's been hundreds of years since we spoke. I don't know where she is, though I'm sure a tour of the world's most respected museums would turn her up, probably in the centre of a great, vaulted chamber, flanked by lesser creations than herself. The museum's curator knowing he has something very special, but never quite knowing what she is, who she is.

I think of my father. His rough hands and suspicious eyes. Mortal, he's long gone, of course, but I owe everything I have, and everything I've lost, to his skills and his prayers – and his lusts.

The captain of the ship approaches to stand beside me, and consider the stars also. I'm new here, but I'm also very old, and the others on the ship seem to understand that. As usual, they show me great deference and respect, even if they don't know why. I don't look like the type to work on a fishing ship, I never have. I should be performing on a stage somewhere, or posing for photographs, but the men always seem to know, to sense, that I belong on the sea. No captain has ever turned me away when asked if I could join his crew.

'It's a nice night for the stars,' he says. Small talk. Prattle. No reason to be rude, though. If there is one thing I've learned over three thousand years on fishing ships, it's that politeness goes a long way to keeping a ship functioning.

'It is,' I say, putting a smile into my voice.

'Thinking of home?' he asks.

'Yes.' I say, 'Always.'

'You can't go back, you know?'

I turn to look at him then. His sharp-featured profile reminds me of my husband, a sculptor and a leader of men, like my father. A man whose selfishness and hubris defined the most important moments of his life and his death, also like my father. It's not the first time I've noticed the similarities, but it always feels like a fresh revelation.

'No, I can't,' I say, 'but how would you know that?'

It is his turn to smile at the sky. 'No one can, right?' he says. 'No matter where we go, when we return, home has changed, we have changed. That place in our minds that we call home: that's the only place it exists.'

One of my daughters comes to alight by his hand on the railing and caws at him. He shoos her away without malice. 'What is with the gulls, this run?' he asks idly.

'They follow me,' I tell him.

He chuckles, thinking it a joke. He turns to look at me. His face is aged and craggy, toughened by the wind and sun and salt. Nothing like my husband.

'Have you tried?' I ask him.

'Once or twice,' he admits with a frown and a shrug. 'Never worked.'

'I've never tried,' I tell him. 'I knew, the moment my home was lost to me.'

'Want to tell me about it?'

I search the man's face for motive, but find nothing. What would I tell him? The truth?

'My husband was murdered,' I begin.

'I'm sorry,' he says with a frown.

'It was his own fault,' I say. 'He betrayed very powerful men and they took their revenge.'

'I see,' he says, clearly unsure of how to react. Not the story he was expecting, perhaps?

'The true tragedy is my daughters,' I tell him, holding out my hand for one of them to perch, and I stroke her feathers, holding her close to my face. 'They've never been the same since.' I kiss her lightly on the brow.

He has no words for me this time. He stares at my daughter, frowning. I lift my hand, and she rises back to join her sisters in their eternal circling.

The captain and I both turn back to the stars. After a very long moment, he says, 'I hope, someday, that you and your girls find peace.'

'Someday,' I agree, but I don't believe it. I don't know what it would take. Three thousand miles and three thousand years from home, if we haven't found peace yet, we never will.

The Captain stays to watch the stars with me for a few minutes longer, but he is weary and his head droops. Unlike me, he needs sleep. He bids me goodnight, and walks back toward his cabin. I watch the stars, listen to my daughters, and think of home. And I wonder how we can ever find peace.

Listen, Noah's Wife
Roppotucha Greenberg

He'll install a foghorn to sound every night. Contain yourself. Slip into the dreams of the river: how it knocked on your window, how the elephants' trunks stretched above the waves, and the last helicopters hummed and gulped and mourned the land. No, you chose not to go into the ark, and rightly so. But you remember how it was built, every timber frame and righteous prayer. How YouTube spoke from on high, and he listened, but not to you. And all the pipes of the house agreed and burst. And you made clumsy footprints on the lino and let the tap drip.

Up in the green water, he'll complain that you never kept the Lego tidy. They're using it to patch up the ship every time another animal escapes. They're down to bits with wheels, ice-creams, and the mysterious ones with playdough in the bumps. It's lopsided, trying too hard, more submarine than ark really. Your giant face is below them, the torrents above, all the birds are cooing, and the dishes are piling up. You still want to help? He still wants to save? Soft. Turn your thoughts into jellyfish bubbles.

Other families had it worse. Husbands joining the army, how would you like that? Wives turning into many rhinoceros. But this is home: brackish waters, pasty arguments over newspapers good-only-to-wrap-fish-in, mizzle. And the little shares and likes of other people's hate, drip-dripping into your marriage. And the day of the bad joke, and the day the TV reared and threatened to swallow its young.

Stay still, let the barnacles rest on your thighs and the octopi snuggle in your hair. Hear the anglerfish speak. Let the small particles of you fall into the bathypelagic zone, like snow. He thinks the flood is real, but it's only a myth. Dark as myth, dirty as myth, full of drowned fish. It will soon recede, and the new land will rise about you in stiff peaks. And the blank light that coats your world now will shatter into colour.

The Fisherman's Wife
Linda McMullen

When I met my husband, he was a modest clerk at a promising company. I learned too late that was not the same thing as being a promising clerk at a modest company. Soon after we married, he was dismissed. That's what he said…

….as if he hadn't been sacked.

He took up his father's trade and became a fisherman. I found myself bitterly regretting that I had fallen for his charming words hook, line, and sinker. So, there we were, netting nothing. Living in a piss-pot.

I amassed the leavings from his catch – miniscule shrimp, fish too small to fry – and tossed them in a pot. I added salt, onions, and kitchen-garden herbs, and sold the stock to a restaurant. His fish sales and my earnings just kept us.

One day – amazingly! – my husband caught a fish with the prince's missing ring in its mouth. The poor dullard wanted to simply return it! I encouraged him – using my wifely wiles – to seek a reward. He resisted. I persisted. He finally agreed. He came home with a few coins and a new fishing net.

Idiot.

I 'appropriated' his coins and bought milk, paper, ink, glue, and a pen. I sold the milk to the neighbours for their skinny children. I collected the now-empty bottles and affixed handmade labels: *Missus Hannah's Fish Stock*. Then I hiked to the hotel and sold the stock at a tidy profit.

My husband called it dubious.

I called it enterprising.

I bought more milk bottles and sold the milk as before. I labelled them *Missus Hannah's Famous Fish Stock* and touted their robust flavour to the overpaid cooks in gentlemen's kitchens. They were happy to spend a little money to save time. The bottles sold for ten times what the restaurant paid.

My husband said: That's not right, Hannah.

And I said: If it weren't worth that, they wouldn't pay it.

And so my business grew, and I moved us into a cottage at the edge of town. Fish stews were all the rage among the gentry in those days; I hired a boy to walk among the piss-pot neighbours we'd left behind, to swap milk for the fishermen's remainders. I bought a cauldron. My husband suggested uneasily that my acumen resembled sorcery. I suggested briskly that he take a long stroll off a short pier.

Soon we could afford a proper house, and a plot of land next to it; I grew my own onions and herbs. I built a shed to store the produce and house a kitchen: there, the boy and I could tend several cauldrons at once.

I began producing vegetable stocks, too.

My husband retreated to the piss-pot. He began spreading some wild story that I thought I was greater than God, but, truth be told, I didn't care. I was quite happy to leave him to flounder.

Ballast
Diana Powell

Let me speak to you about the sea – how I always loved it.

I dressed up in my brother's clothes to go there.

Took my mother's shears, and put them to my scalp, and closed the blades to.

Dug up the coin my father stashed for his ale, put it in a purse tied round my waist, then left.

I headed for the nearest port, signed up on the earliest ship. They didn't look too hard. They wanted hands, even those undersized and smooth. I wondered if there were more like me on board.

There weren't; not then.

I wondered, too, if I would meet monsters. They were said to live in the farthest reaches, beyond the edge of any map. They had the faces of devils, the might of giants and the ways of foul beasts. I did not expect to see them closer to shore, closer to me.

The sea. I licked my tongue across the rim of it, as soon as I could taste. I clenched my toes in the yielding bottoms of its shallows, before I could walk two steps.

And when I swam out into it, soon after that roiling gait, I felt the welcome of it on my skin. I was born different, my mother always hinted, for I was one of those who kept the caul around me, even after she had pushed me forth. Perhaps it was this that marked me out – floating in the birth-water longer than most, my lungs seasoned to it, my limbs free.

Something else it meant, she said, as she presented me with its desiccated scraps, when I was grown enough for reason – death by drowning would not be my fate.

'Keep it safe. Or sell it if you need money!' Our superstitions shifted with the wind and need. Still, I hid it deep, in that leather purse, rather than add its value to my own daily bread or drink. It seemed the right thing to do, considering my destination, my ambition. And yes, when I finally stood on deck in the middle of a distant ocean, and saw how the water there owned a different nature from the one caressing the shore and my body, I gave thanks to the sea gods for it, and any extra charm they might bestow.

And I thought the men around me would be glad, too, if they knew. There was none as superstitious as a sailor, I soon learnt. 'Fair enough,' I thought, now that I had eyed the measure of that deep. 'Let them fear their Jonahs, keep to their lucky days, pray to their favoured saints.'

Yet I laughed to myself over the predilections of such muscle-bound, full-of-themselves creatures that the 'weaker' sex must always obey. So much for men.

Men – that brother I'd grown up with, the father who'd sired me – I thought I knew enough of them. But perhaps these sailors were a different caste from those who stayed land-locked and lubberly. A breed with strange ways, as well as those odd, fateful imaginings.

Still, I discovered a fondness for the garments they wore. I liked the hug of the breeches round my legs, dependable, instead of fooling me, like a wayward skirt. I liked the boots, wide and flat, so that my gait was firm and square instead of the dallying mince a woman must dance. Better still, away from land, all footwear was shed, the easier to climb and cling to the slimy deck, rope and masts. I remembered the clenching of my toes in the sand, and felt that freedom again. It was there, too, in the looseness of the smock, letting my skin and lungs breathe. And there was another advantage – how it, together with the jerkin I wore, was a useful shield for the swell of my breasts. Still, there was little enough to hide; I had always been of boyish build. And I used other wiles to aid my disguise – gave myself out as a shy young lad, even a bit slow in the head; excuses to keep to myself. It worked well enough that first voyage, kept on working, even when war came.

A new ship followed, a new captain, a new purpose, sending us back to our own coast. Strange, that the worst weather the sea could offer came to us then.

The storm hit us somewhere off the tip of the land, chaining us to port, instead of easing our fury in the promised fight. Was that it? Was that what the men felt? Some brimming, boiling need, waiting to be assuaged? I knew something of it, of course, with my brother the other side of the bed, the sounds from my father the other side of the curtain. But this...?

I wasn't with them when they went ashore, claiming the post of watch, as I so often did – another excuse for staying apart. But I saw their return, the women pushed and dragged, heard the cries, guessed the blood. And I saw from their clothing that most were nuns, and learnt from the talk of the pillage of a convent and its nearby church. And I thought I, and they, these Holy 'Virgins', had now seen the worst of men. What other horrors could they unleash, after that?

There are as many ways of falling as there are of walking, running, flying. I saw them all that day. We had set sail, could linger no longer, even though the weather was bleaker still. We were needed for the battle, as if the sea would acquiesce to man's need. Instead, it rose higher, twisted lower, thrashed deeper than I had ever seen it. And the ship, too low, too heavy in the water, on account of the extra cargo, was happy to sink into it, without protest.

So let me tell you about falling.

They began one by one. Two of the greatest hulks taking an arm each of the fullest woman, as if it were no more than a question of weight, of ballast – the abbess I guessed she must be, on account of that indulgent girth. No matter who, they dragged her to the side, shoving her up, then over. The first… A languid tumble, that one, head over heels; her mind, perhaps, not grasping what was happening to her. So, somehow, in the descent, her bulbous flesh could do what it would never do on land, as if there were something in the air giving spring to her fleshy limbs.

A scramble of arms and legs, the next one, as if she were trying to climb frantically back up an invisible mast, back into the arms of those who had thrown her; those who looked down on her, and laughed.

Some stayed stiff, arms tight to their sides, legs and feet close together, and plummeted like an arrow, hardly furrowing the water beneath. Others curled up, like the baby born too soon I once saw, a sister or brother I should have had.

I thought – *They will stop. That's enough. The load has lightened, surely. The boat has risen in the water.*

It was then that I heard the rumour of the men, whittled out between their laughs and their shouts. It was not that the weight was more or that their worth was less than a cask of rum or a sack of grain. No, their fate was sealed simply on account of what they did not conceal in manly clothes, under the protection a charm – their sex; as if the crew had suddenly recalled their strongest superstition – *A woman on board brings bad luck to a ship.*

I thought – *No, you cannot do this. I cannot do this – I must do something. I must call the captain. I must…*

What? Declare that I was a woman, too, and had sailed with them in the calmest seas, the best of times?

Instead, I just kept on watching. And they kept on falling.

There was one who hit the side of the ship on the way down – I heard the crack of her head, even above the wind and the waves. I saw the slide of her downwards, and hoped she might be lucky, and had died there and then.

There was another who hit the side gently, and managed somehow to grab the rigging, and haul herself up. I wanted to cheer her on, until I saw the face of the man waiting for her. Then I found myself whispering 'Go back.' Wasn't the fate of the sea better? Wasn't drowning to be preferred?

There are as many ways of drowning, as there are of falling… when it begins, at least; in that first contact with the water, the way the body hits. Flat, with a thud, like the fat boys jumping off the wharf we always laughed at, that first one – the 'may-be' Abbess. Her agile tumbling ceased as she made her approach, her arms spread out, her belly hit first. The ripples fanned… a slow, wide collapse of the water. Or that plummeting arrow, straight and clean. I saw the clambering girl still scramble in the water, so that she stayed on the surface for a while, in some kind of semblance of a paddling dog. She might have made something of it, if the water had been calm, if we'd been closer to the shore. Was she still paddling away, once she went under? How long for her, how long for any of them, before the water entered each and every orifice of their bodies, and drove the air out of nose, mouth and lungs, finding its way, slowly at first, then faster, reclaiming them back to their birth, in death.

Did they pray, I wondered? These women of God who believed in Him, as we all should? But hadn't they prayed before, when the sailors first appeared? What good had it done them? And when they thought it was over, to find themselves taken – did they still pray then? And when they were pulled onto the deck, and forced off the side, as they were falling, as they hit the water, and they sank under, so that every last breath was needed for living, did they still pray then?

Prayer made no difference in the end, but neither did superstition – or was my disguise, good enough to fool men, laughed at by the sea? The storm grew worse, the wind stronger, the waves wilder. It blew us across the channel to Ireland, and drove us onto that country's toothsome rocks, waiting to crunch the boats and our bodies apart.

When I came to, I dragged myself up, and began to walk away from the shore. I paid no attention to any others lying there. I didn't care if they were alive or dead. I walked, taking the charity of strangers, and made my way to the nearest port, and crossed back to England, but I didn't return home. Instead, I kept on walking, from village to village, and town to town, and everywhere I went, I told what I had seen.

Let me tell you about the sea. How I don't go there anymore.

My brother's clothes were long gone, ripped apart on a foreign shore.

In time, my hair was grown again.

I sold the caul from my leather pouch, and kept the money there, for my most basic of needs.

I had discovered that women were not wanted on board ship.

And I knew that there were monsters, with faces like devils, and the foulest of ways.

In 1379, an English fleet, under the command of Sir John Arundel, was to be sent in support of the Duke of Brittany, against the French. However, a violent storm blew the ships west, and caused them to wreck on the Irish coast, with most lives lost.

Froissart, and other chroniclers of the period, mention nothing of the pillage of a convent, and the killing of its nuns. And, indeed, there is little evidence of the existence of a nunnery in this location.

However, Thomas Walsingham, a monk of St Albans abbey, includes the story in his 'Cronica maiora', saying he learnt it from some who were there, and there was no reason to disbelieve them.

In 2015, human smugglers, travelling from Libya, threw pregnant women and children overboard, to force commercial ships to rescue them.

The Surgeon's Mate
Maria Kyle

'Tis no easy matter to cut off a man's leg. 'Tis harder still amid the splinter and crash of a sea-battle, when a pall of powder smoke hangs in the tweendecks black as a Tahitian pearl, and the shrieks of men dying and damning razor your ears raw, and the thud of your own blood in your skull pounds like a brass cannon till the Devil himself might be screaming you down to hell and you would not know but by the shape of his black lips.

But it can be done. Ay, and it must, and swiftly, if Olsson is not to lose his life into the bargain; and Olsson is a first mate worth a score of any other beggar aboard. Barnacles the lot of 'em, clinging to this old tub for their worthless lives, doing not a cursed thing for their loot-shares but slowing her clip and quaffing her rum.

Two of the crew pin Olsson down as he thrashes and raves, and I never saw grown men pale so quick at the glimpse of a bone-saw. The only thing sailors hate worse than water, in my experience, is blood, and the musket-ball's torn through an artery, smashing the bone, Olsson's thigh jetting crimson like a whale in spout.

Through the smoke and madness, I spy a seaman cowering 'neath a splintered cannon-port, half-black with gunpowder and shaking worse than the ship.

'Here, you swab!' I yell. Even over the din of shot and tearing timber, my roar's the match of any fishmaid's at Billingsgate mart, and he scuttles across the yawing gun-deck crabwise, eyes huge and white in the gloaming.

'Doctor?'

'Take this!' The ligature I've lashed about Olsson's thigh has slipped, his every convulsion slackening it and spraying me and my shuddering helpmeets with more of God's good wine. I hand the lad one end of the cord and haul on the other like I'm raising the topgallant in the teeth of a storm. Tighter, tighter, taut as a corset-string, and at last tied, slick with blood and sweat and Christ knows what else; but the red fountain falters and Olsson falls back, and if I am to save him the moment is now.

I press a bottle of rum to his lips, make sure he swallows, then shove in a wooden peg for him to bite down upon.

'Hold him still, damn you!' I growl at all three sailors as I lift the saw. Swift, savage and sure the cut must be, for the femur is ebony-hard and will not

21

strike its flag at the first blow. The leg itself is a slaughterman's nightmare, shattered above the knee in a raspberry pulp of flesh and pale bone-pips. As with a broken spar, I must trim the splinters by cutting above the break, and do it quick and rough – two minutes at the outside. For though Olsson lies half-dead there are men worse off than he, and the well-armed merchantman that locks us in bloody embrace is making more of 'em each moment.

The saw's first stroke falls like an axe-blow, and Olsson bucks wildly, six inches straight up, a great low sound like a bull's groan bellowing twixt his clamped teeth.

'Hold him I say!' Hold him as a drowning man cleaves to a rope, as a priest to God or gold, as a pirate to rum; for there are half a dozen more strokes to come. 'Tis a big limb on a big man, a thick and sturdy bone. 'Twill be no easy matter. But it must and can be done.

On a ship like ours, every man's both equal and unequal: has a vote and a share and a job and a station, but the first mate's loss cannot be allowed– for my own sake more even than the crew's. Because Olsson cannot die. He is the only one who knows what I am.

*

It was Tom who first lit upon the notion of sailing with gentlemen of fortune (as he always romantically styled pirates) 'stead of the Navy vessels he trained upon, after the death of Lieutenant Hayes aboard the Belligerent. 'Twas in no wise his fault; the boy was gut-shot, threequarters in the ground before Tom touched him, but his father Admiral Hayes never forgave the loss.

A starveling year followed, in which no King's ship would touch Tom, no more than if he was a woman or a leper, till I told him straight out he'd to find another calling, or else consign our own son, ay, and ourselves too, to a pauper's grave. Portsmouth had land-surgeons enough, and so Tom eked a wage as a dockyard labourer while I sewed and young Jos studied. But by the hard winter of 'nineteen our bodies and souls were barely on nodding terms.

'Tom,' I said, over porridge that was more water and wishes than milk-and-oats, 'hell or high-water, you must get a berth somehow or we'll not outlive Michaelmas.'

He sighed, his lean face stubbled for want of a razor worth the name, and pale as the snowfilled sky. 'I know it, Jess. And I'll find one, you may lay to it. Soon.'

I squeezed his hand: 'twas like a clutch of tinder-twigs. 'Very well, my love.

But wherever you sign on, take Josiah with you. I'll manage without him here. He's fourteen now and needs man's rations: it chokes me to see him stinted so.'

Tom's frown bit deeper. 'Take him along? As what? Cabin-boys are common as weevils, and Jos has never sailed. He's handy and bright enough, but 'tis too late to apprentice him to a carpenter or cook—'

'Then apprentice me to yourself, Father.' Jos spoke for the first time; till now he had been following our talk with a listlessness bailed out of hope, but now his blue eyes, too great in that thin wan face, glittered alive.

'Take you on…?'

'Ay!' He balled his skinny fists in eagerness. 'On Navy ships surgeons have mates, ain't they?'

'Some,' Tom admitted, 'the larger ones. And if not, a loblolly boy at least. But those lads are seamen first and medical thereafter… Besides, they're properly apprenticed, trained, experienced—'

'Then train me! I can learn, and fast, you know that: I've studied half your books besides, for what else excepting the Bible is there on a drear night to pass the time?'

Tom looked across at Jos sharply; their two keen profiles like those scissored-paper dolls that copy themselves perfectly. 'Have you now? Didn't know you'd found the bookcase-key.'

'Ma gave it me,' Jos said without a blink.

'He reads aloud as I sew, and we discuss it together, quite like two physicians at the Royal College,' I explained.

'Do you indeed?' Tom was fast crossing the line twixt amusement and amazement, and I tamped down my pride in Jos as he stared at his father levelly, inviting any objection.

'I do, Pa. And I want to assist you.' His enthusiasm broke the surface, a fish twisting and flashing in the sun. 'I'd give anything!'

And he did. O Lord, alas, he did.

*

Tom promised me he'd find a ship to take him on 'even if I must sail with the worst crew on the wave'.

'Lord forbid it come to that,' I'd answered; but a mere month after, he made good his word. The bitter coastal cold was gnawing in earnest the night he returned with the news: the *Galant* was weighing anchor tomorrow week, and had urgent need of a sea-surgeon, having lost hers in a deadly encounter off the Italian coast. An assistant, too, was not felt superfluous, and Jos would earn half of what Tom made if he joined the crew. It was manna, it was a white dove, a rainbow: it was all the things I'd prayed for without daring to dream of. And of course, like the rainbow, 'twas pure mirage. For it was from that night that the awful curse of the *Galant* began to lick about our three lives like the tentacles of a great grim Leviathan, rising slowly from the depths until it could engulf us whole.

My gratitude to God for His succour did not long survive Tom's confession that the *Galant* was no simple merchantman: in truth, she was in plain terms a smuggling-ship, bent for France to exchange our good English gold for French wine, brandy and silks, without troubling the King or especially the Exchequer for such trifles as a trading licence or permission. No wonder she lost surgeons in sea-battles – smugglers were pirates sailing under another flag, so far as I was concerned!

I hardly could credit that Tom had cast in his lot with such a crew, but if 'tis steal or starve – and so, in those lean and awful months, it seemed to be – 'better to crib tax from a King and government who need it not,' urged Tom, 'than thieve from our own neighbours, who live or die by every bite of bread.' Still, it was a bitter cup, and I gagged on the notion that our son should sail with outlaws unawares. I need not have troubled my conscience, in the end.

Yet I did not, could not tell Jos: his hectic delight in the new appointment, after four weeks' apprenticeship with his father in the art of assisting a surgeon, had him flitting about our dark little rooms for all the world like a butterfly just unfurled. Tom and he visited sick sailors in their lodging-houses by way of practice and training, to study and attempt to alleviate the common diseases of the seafaring life. Once in a way they'd glean a few pennies for their trouble, but it was no sort of living – and it was in one of these dank hovels that Jos caught the fever that would take him afore he ever stepped foot on a ship.

Three days and nights Tom and I nursed him, without sleep, food or rest ourselves, and on the third he burned up just like a twist of paper in the chimney, and his soul flew straight to heaven, as sparks from a great blaze rise and are lost in the darkness. When he was gone, I stayed with my wet cheek pressed to his scorching hand, until the warmth began to ebb and my knees to stiffen. Then I rose and took off my apron, and walked down to the whispering white beach and into the sea. Tom caught up with me, plunging madly through the icy surf, only when the waves were lapping up to my chin. He wrenched me about and tried to pull me back towards shore, but I held up my hands and he dropped his.

''Tis no good,' I said. 'Jos is gone, and you are going. I would have missed you both but now I have lost you both. And I will be a sea-widow, poor and friendless, and you'll be in danger every moment, and I cannot bear you to die too.'

He shook his wet head violently, and the moon smacked from a tear-glint in his eyes. 'No, my love. I'll not go now, how can I? We'll stay and mourn our boy, and – and I will find something, we will –'

'We'll die too!' I cried, my voice savage above the sea's snarl. 'Go! You must go. Only leave me!'

He would not leave me. He could no more swim than I, but somehow he thrashed us both back through the shallows and up the shore, where we lay bone-chilled and exhausted and weeping while our son's body cooled in the bitter little rooms we had once called home.

Tom dragged me to a low sort of tavern and filled us both with rough smuggled brandy we could ill afford, and we talked and wept until we knew what we should do. So, Tom went to join the *Galant* and, in place of Jos, I went along too.

A Madras Crossing
Elizabeth Hopkinson

Eleanor

I thought the worst of the voyage was over when we weighed anchor off the coast of Madras. How ignorant I am, even after eight months at sea! I am in Hell. Surely we will die in these roiling waves. The boat ahead of us is half-capsized. The wind carries their screams in snatches. Major Hardcastle has already offered the native boatmen double if they can bring us to shore unharmed.

I do not know what they say to him in reply. Their tongue sounds harsh, angry. They are almost completely naked. What would Mamma say to that? I try not to look at their muscular chests, their brown legs. Salt stings my eyes. My gown is soaked through to the petticoat. Perhaps we should all go naked. Perhaps I should stand on the beach like Eve in her glory and wait for a husband to carry me away.

Eliza

Eight months ago, my name was Maryam and I was a Muslim. Now my name is Eliza and I am a Christian. Papa-ji has changed his mind so many times, I no longer know who or what I am.

The Hopewell lies at anchor, beyond reach of the pounding surf. From here, it looks like one of those ships in a bottle that Papa-ji's friend, Dr Lennox, showed to me. It is strange. I have seen so many East Indiamen come and go from the harbour. But I have never once set foot aboard. Where will I sleep? What will I eat? I wonder if the food will be halal, and then remember that halal no longer matters. Or does it? No, Charles says they know nothing about halal in Scotland.

Charles has always been Charles. Not Ali or Saeed or Imran. Charles will inherit Father's estate, no matter that his skin is browner than mine. If I were browner, I would have been spared this voyage. But then Charles would have to travel alone, to a country neither of us has seen.

Eleanor

If Mamma had any notion what life aboard an East Indiaman is like, she would not have been so keen to send me on this journey. She who cares so much for propriety! There is no privacy at sea. Sailors deprived of their wives and sweethearts care not what they say to a woman. Or what they touch, if you don't stop them. Maria, Catherine and I – the three brides-to-be – took to shutting ourselves in our cabin, eating our meals in there and bringing them back up, as likely as not. And if we became particularly cosy during the long watches of the night, who is to know? Or care?

'You are twenty-nine years old, Eleanor,' Mamma said to me. 'Do you wish to become a burden on your family? Our men in the East Indies are crying out for brides. You will board that ship and you will do your duty.'

Will the men in India be kinder, more tolerant than the men of Yorkshire? Will I meet a husband who will let me be myself?

Eliza

I fidget in my new clothes. They are too hot, too constraining. Mrs Lennox says she will help me with the stays until I get used to them. I begged Mamma-ji, could I not wear my sari until we reach European waters? She simply kept cutting and stitching, following Mrs Lennox's paper pattern.

'It is important,' she said, 'that you look like a proper Scottish lady from the start. Because that is what you are, beti. You are going to have an education and a wonderful life.'

There were tears in her eyes when she said this. I don't want a wonderful life if it means leaving Sharena behind. Sharena looks too Indian, Papa-ji says.

'You may think it a kindness to let Sharena come with you,' Papa said. 'But it would be a cruelty. Edinburgh society would never accept her, with so dark a cheek. She would be an object of mockery wherever she went. I would not have that for my daughter. Besides, who will comfort your mother?'

Who will comfort me? Not Charles. When we reach Scotland, we will be sent to school, but it will not be the same school, of course, and not even in the same town. Charles says that Scotland is cold and rainy, with hairy cattle and deer that bellow. I am afraid to go there, far from the chittering of monkeys and Mamma's lullaby.

Eleanor

Ashore at last! The boat lists to one side as the anchor goes down. More semi-clad men come running up the beach, bringing a stepladder for us to disembark, offering to take our luggage. I hitch up my sodden skirt, swaying on my feet.

'See, the palanquin has come for us,' Major Hardcastle says. 'You'll be perfectly safe now, ladies.'

Beyond the beach, white walls gleam. The sky is a dazzling blue. Heat like the exhalation of a dragon breathes over us. A dragon with talons that are reaching out to take me in.

How will I survive in this strange new land?

Eliza

The boats are ready for us now. Aboard the East Indiaman, a striped flag flutters in the growing breeze.

Charles takes me by the elbow as I mount the ladder. Whalebone cracks against my ribs. I am surrounded by the sea, without, within. The breakers roll, foaming up the beach. I am being set adrift in a vast world I know nothing about.

Men call to us from the Indiaman as we ride the surging waves. So many men! In Mamma-ji's part of the house, we were all women together. Now there is just me and Mrs Lennox. I want Sharena. I feel so alone.

How will I survive in a strange new land?

Man Overboard
Emily Bullock

Deptford, 1800

All dreams of death can be forgotten on waking, except when under that final sleep from which there is no waking and only a long forgetting. This is the thought that's kept me awake for five nights.

Is it day yet? Hard to tell in this curtained berth at the mission. I lie on my back. Darkness lies back on me, thick as tar. Stuck to the bed.

I pinch the skin on my knuckles. Awake, not dead then. Either way, they'll find me with boots on, coat on. The buttons dig into my chin. I'd like to see the man could take my uniform from me. If ever I do, he'll likely be from a place such as this.

The Seaman's Mission is the black depths. The Seaman's Mission is my sanctuary.

I don't know how I came to be here.

I do know, but I don't want to remember. Not that swirling hell. Not that stink of death. Onwards, to blue water for me. I punch the straw bedding. I must return to ship, the land is no good for me, the city is eating me – that can't be true, it's the bad beef pie, it's the booze, only the pie was all swede and gravy and the rum was watered down.

I sit up. Head knocking the bunk above.

I'm really feeling much better.

I lie down.

Death is waiting for me on the other side of the curtain.

Or is this the dream?

No sooner am I down the mission stairs than my new mess mates are there to fetch me. Usually I like to choose my own mates when I meet a fresh crew but they seem a jolly pair, and I've just come from a hot smothered dream, and feel in no mood to set them right.

I've no use for mates now, let this lot have me. Rather a hammock and crow's foot biscuits than the dead air of the mission. I set a brisk pace, swing my arms, happy that I'm off to sea again.

A carriage, horses, plump fellows bouncing beside me.

Almost a ship. Back and forth we go. Up and down.

Street and dust.

Can't see what's out there. Nothing is still. Nothing's been still for many a month.

Close my eyes.

Use my hands as anchor, clutched fists in my pockets.

The journey passes as journeys do.

The carriage stops. They make a show of holding open the door, taking my arm, helping me to the ship. Which isn't needed but strikes me as a friendly gesture.

So, I'm on board. Only yesterday I thought I'd never put out of harbour again, and now my new mates are leading me through the ship. Let the wind blow, let the currents run, I'll find what I'm hunting far out across the waves.

Of course, I'm grateful to be here, but it's a strange place, dark and sodden. A 74-gun ship of the third rate, going by the size of these decks. I can usually tell from her shadow but I don't recall catching sight of her before stepping below.

The sailors about this place have shaved heads. Must have been lice. Some ships get like that after many months at sea. It would never happen on Captain Bligh's watch, too fond of the vinegar.

I thought the mission meant to keep me from a commission. I misjudged them.

Thank God no one there got the thought to lock me up in a madhouse. I've seen them do that to troublesome old salts. I'm not old yet but I've been feeling rougher than the last sea-biscuit in the barrel.

This is just what I need, time at sea. Though how we got from Deptford to Portsmouth so quick I don't recall. A fast carriage, fresh horses can do it in less time than you'd think these days.

It's the fever stealing hours from me.

Losing time used to be fatal at sea, a sailor could get too far off course to navigate his way home. They have clocks now that keep ship's time. I've seen them for myself. I don't suppose this old girl has one. She's broken down like privateers have sucked the marrow from her bones. There's some about this place, lying on the deck, look all skin and bone. Flog the cook. Him there has a bleeding sore on his scalp. Damn the surgeon.

My skin itches.

Dirty lice.

Getting a bad feeling.

Guts are churning.

They march me on. The deck runs and runs.

Something's sour – stinks like a plague of rats died in the ballast. Men lie about like there's no work to be done. Where's the watch? How deep down in the hold are we? Can't hear the sea's heartbeat. That lamp, shining too white, burns me. That crow at the window stares into me. Hands dig into my arms.

I'm a marine not a prisoner.

Left standing with your cock in your hand, that's you, James Norris.

I'll not answer, not now I'm on my way again.

The crow pecks at the glass. Only the Captain's rooms have windows, why are we going there?

Sign me up, what else do I have? But don't take me to the Captain. I'm not fit to be seen. What's left of me? I've got no sides to hold anything in. Look how my arms and legs shimmer. If my new mess mates step away, I'll splash to the floor.

I'm a drowning man. I'm drowning, man! Nothing but spit comes out.

Those doors up there, what's behind them?

Am I watched?

The boards beneath my feet are rotten, they'll not survive the pitch and roll of a storm.

Down to the lower deck. Least those doors can't spy me here. No hammocks up yet, always hard to tell night from day down below.

There's another door.

I'm not liking the look of this.

I've signed up with a bad lot. Not a decent red uniform between them. I'm the only man with his boots and buttons ready for inspection. But she's a big ship. Can't even reach the planks above. A grand old lady.

My messmates drag me on.

'Do you think I'm green?' I say, trying to pull away. They've got quite the pinch on me.

That door, all carved wood, big locks, is getting closer. Two sailors stand side by side in front of it, looking like some double headed dog monster.

'Listen, you bastards.' I try to prise their fingers off my arms. 'Don't I know my way round a ship?'

They laugh at that, but they're not so jolly as I first thought. Four of them now, and me – not best odds. But all about this place look like misery kicked them in the arse. The cracked wood, the rat shit, and straw – no sailor lets straw lie on the floor. They must have had a bad, bad voyage of it. This is my last chance, too late once they have me through that door... anything could be on the other side.

One of sailors in the doorway beckons. 'Don't fight it,' he says.

Why would he say that? My father used to say that. I turn my head, twist my neck but there's no clock to set on this ship. Time is slipping again. If we sail soon perhaps I'll be saved. I have to leave behind that darkness, those dreams...

'Seaward, boys,' I call.

It's not professional to be escorted like this, even if it is in jest. And it isn't like me to allow it. But I'm sweating, my legs shake a little, fever burns under my nails. I've not slept enough. My body's thick with waking. My new mess mates pull away, leave me standing there like I'm pissing into the wind. Slow, if only everything would slow. But I don't like to be late. Captain Bligh never tolerated lateness. Everything had to be in the correct place at the correct time. These sailors are expecting me, they take hold of my arms.

They're taking me through that door. I don't want to enter. What's waiting on the other side? Tell me that.

Tell me something.

The fever scorches me, hot as a fired cannon. They'll have to let go soon or I'll melt their flesh. They shove me. Caught by the two sailors now, fixed tight. Dragged inside the door.

Black as a bilge hole.

Black enough to make a man forget who he is. But I'll never forget what I'm after.

I brace my arms against the frame. One grabs my neck, forces it forward. The other kicks at my legs. They'll not get me in there.

For a moment, in that darkness, I think I see my father standing up ahead. I remember how it was back then. Only seventeen, thinking I was a man. A young buck hobbled by having an old goat so close. He's the reason I became a marine. All the way to the docks, signing up with a fishing boat, sailing off the Boston coast, further into the Atlantic, praying to any god who'd listen to let the English find me, let the navy have me. Through seasickness, through storms, I asked myself the same questions: What are you James Norris? Your father's shadow, less of a man than a lesser man? Or are you a fighter? Don't you want to be something?

The English boarded us on the second month at sea. They called out for any not free born. I was English made if not born – it was a small lie, only what they wanted to hear.

I became a marine that day, answered their cry, Come boys, who's for blue water?

I shake my head. That's all done with, I made my choices. A man can't win a fight against the past as it is what it is, no changing it. But the past has a way of lashing out, slicing you open – it wants you to bloody brawl.

I feel the same now as I did when a boy, on board a strange ship. Sweat sticks the shirt to my back. Someone take me to sea. And all I have to do is

follow them, walk through this darkness. How can I do anything else?
    I shout out, 'Come boys, who's for blue water?'

They say I'm mad.
I say they're mad.
I lost the flip.
That's me locked up in Bethlem Hospital.
'Come boys, who's for Bedlam?'
Maybe I am what they say I am.
I was never a good man.
No, that can't be true.
I've left footprints on a glacier.
I've seen the sun burst out of the Atlantic.
I've eaten sweet papaya from a low hanging tree in Tahiti.
I've glimpsed Paradise.
Life made sense when I was all at sea.

*Inspired by James Norris: American, Marine in the Royal Navy,
inmate of Bethlem Hospital for the insane.*

Remittance
Kilmeny MacMichael

Sir inform have not received expected amount this first of month reason

Regret inform amount adjusted due understanding of your current circumstance

Sir your understanding my circumstances must be more positive than mine

Sir monies sent will not cover current and next bills

Sir funds received only half expected cut severe unreasonable why

Sir have been ill unable to work doctor to pay

Sir full promised funds required need urgent

Suggest lack of economy evident in overuse of words if finances desperate advise restraint of expensive telegraphic correspondence

Sir full promised funds required urgent

Have received reliable information your recent expenditures and activities such cannot in good consciousness continue previous generous support amount sent believed sufficient for modest living

Regret your informer mustnt be as well informed as you evidently believe disheartened you employ spy do not trust me

Need you be reminded circumstances which led to your emigration trust impossible

Sir was youthful misunderstanding this not the same I assure

Sir what usage questioned bad winter many head lost must rebuild good opportunity now but fleeting funding urgent send funds

Have received unsettling reports of unsuitable company kept and renewed gambling fear

funds requested intended for less than ideal purposes

Sir business opportunity genuine will write details by letter but funding required by sixth or great loss to future prospects here spy may verify

Greatly concerned by reports of your keeping thuggish company

Sir am as circumspect in company kept as country allows

Sir require funds within four days

Report company also taken with entirely unsuitable woman of questionable morals

Sir true I have become acquainted with lady

Understand any new scandal such as previous will not be met with assistance from this quarter will entirely be of your making and repercussions on your head only

Sir true lady is not of good family yet has many fine qualities

Sir although I was at fault with woman known to you previous and behaved badly with this lady all is different good woman though poor as I

Sir may I remind full amount required here sixth only three days remaining

Have report of much undesirable in womans character find most unsuitable

Inform for two months past have been engaged to lady whose virtue you question fear cannot bear further insults

Why must we be informed of such intentions in this way why have you not written earlier seeking advice or declaring purpose

Sir did not wish cause distress as current necessary living arrangements with lady sadly unsavoury due lack of funds

Necessary?

Sir if full funds sent situation remedied with joyous haste intend marriage

So you continue straying and reports of new gambling debts

Sir greater card debts owed to me here then I owe others

Sir offer repayment of funds at interest you set

Suggest seek repayments from local debtors for funding

Sir seeking such would not be wise at this time

What of debts still held for your repayment here

Sir understood regular funding to arrive without fail as agreement at time of my departure do you now renege if so warn I may also

Do not threaten suggest save remittance as has been sent and not waste further on telegrams you will do well to learn habits of husbandry if not month difficult no further help here until next month perhaps your new virtuous woman will be help stay there or consequences

If expected funds not secured will lose all built here begun to build reputation character establish family why now prevent me continuing towards strength cannot make sense done as asked striven to reform

Sir will you not send promised funds

Sir another day is lost send funds

Sir would be shame to send word to grandfather informing your breach of faith regret may find necessary send funds

Do not dare speak to me of shame your mother weeps still for shame you have brought if you are as reformed as you claim with woman good as you say you will show fortitude threats I assure will gain you naught does your good woman know your past

Sir she does finds forgiveness for those past indiscretions has faith in our future pities your lack of compassion

Sir will you not send remainder of promised funds are waited upon by others besides myself others unhappy with delay

One should never promise what one does not have

Sir trusted your word as good as sparrow in hand your betrayal cuts deep send funds

Sir has there been financial catastrophe there too why will you not keep agreement send funds

Sir I beg believe have been ill unable to work

Sir I beg believe will accept whatever little you choose to send in future but now need full expected funds

Sir require funds by end tomorrow

Sir I beseech you not for myself but my wife

Sir without full funds find myself in bodily danger

I bid you good night

Sir do not retire send funds urgent

Sir I beg not for myself but for future of my wife and expected child

Sir I wished not to shock but true child expected

Send funds for love of god

Sir I wished not to shock before but true child is expected surely you will not wish it orphaned

Know you no limit I bid you again good night

Do you truly believe I would lie about child

Father I do not lie need of funds desperate

Father will you not help me

I am sorry for what I have done but it is past I plead for time to prove I will improve I will repay everything possible and vow eternal penance for the rest

Sir for the last time I ask please funds now

Father will you not help me please send funds

Good morning, I trust further funds arrived in time

Fisherfolk
Juliet Humphreys

In Quay Street, when a woman begins to moan with the coming of a child, word goes out. Women — mothers themselves, mostly — congregate in the street outside, right below the window where the woman lies, the better for them to hear. Most often the window is open, whatever the season. This is like as not for the mite to feel the salty air in its lungs.

The crowd bides, sometimes into the morning light. More often babies here come, and sometimes go too, in the space between days.

If the child is well and is heard to cry, the women's quiet chatter explodes with much cheering and, oftentimes, dancing. Then the fiddler from The Swan might be summoned. Some of the women will go home to fetch the blankets they have stitched between them. These gifts are not brought before, for too often they must be given back. Someone might bring a tot of whisky for the pa, if he be around. Mostly there is a pa.

If, after the woman's cries, there is not the sound of a mite, the midwife will shut the window. That is the women's signal to stand close, silent until Dr Musgrove comes. Then the gifts are different.

One Tuesday night in early August, when we are just done with supper, there is a tell-tale double knock at the door. The knocker does not wait but moves on to the next house and the next until all be told.

We have not far to go. Ruby lives but three doors away. Outside her house a crowd has already gathered, their gazes fixed on an upstairs window. It is open wide so we can hear every whimper, every wail; long breaths tearing through the air. Each time there is a pause we are hushed, waiting for the next cry, whether it be ma or mite.

Ruby's husband, Frank Artless, has not the stomach for this and the shrunken shadow of him can be seen pacing the quay. Someone will be sent to fetch him when it is over.

Ruby has a comely shape from carrying a child, but she looks like little more than one herself. She came here from Ireland, but Frank is one of us. He has worked on the boats since he was just a mite aiding his pa, the way they all begin. He and Ruby have not been going together long enough for the child to be his, though no-one would say it aloud — a girl must do as she can. Folk hereabouts wish only that Frank and Ruby be happy. We were all pleased for him when he wed Ruby since he had a wife die before and take the mite too. Private talk was that Frank so wanted to be a pa that he would raise a cuckoo's egg.

Even so, the birthing is too soon, and we know it. We wish ourselves home but will not leave. Going is thought to be a curse.

We have been stood but an hour when Ruby's cries become louder and more frequent.

And then the cries stop. We cease our chatter and wait.

Ruby's scream, when it comes – like a high note held too long – is enough to rip the earth apart. We see the midwife reach up to close the window. With that, Phyllis Smyth turns on her heels to fetch Dr Musgrove while someone else knocks for Phyllis's husband, to fetch Frank and help him home.

As husband and wife start to go their separate ways, we see the midwife come to the window and unlatch it. This can only mean one thing: both are gone. The opening of the window is to allow the souls of the departed to go together.

'The poor child,' folk whisper, meaning Ruby. Too many are lost here for us to mourn those as never lived.

I lie in bed, hearing over and over, Ruby's cry. When I close my eyes, I cannot keep from my mind the picture I have made of the two of them – her and the mite – turning cold. To make it go I rise and tiptoe downstairs to the kitchen.

In homes the length of our street knitted squares await another birthing. They will be pushed out of sight now, and, come first light, ordinary days begun again. I have a small stash of squares. I took especial care with them, they being for Ruby; but they will do just as well for another. In time we will be happy to hear of a coming. The ma, whoever it be, will not wonder whether the squares were made only for her. Though our own blankets may be worn, not one of us would mend them with squares meant for another's mite, not even if they were all we had. There are ways we have, rules that are not weakened from being found nowhere outside of the heart. 'We are fisherfolk,' Mama explained it one time. 'That is all.'

Now in the half-light before dawn I take Ruby's squares from the basket and lay them out on the table. Eleven there are. Three rows of four and one of three. Since I am lost to sleep and even blinking brings back the events of earlier, I pick up a pair of needles and some yarn. There is blue for the bride she was, red for her name, purple for the heather of her homeland – green too – and lastly yellow for the light of her. I will use them all. Row by row as I knit, the square takes on the shape of a prayer. It is all I can do.

Some days in winter the sea rages, sputtering so in our faces that we must wipe its salty spit from our cheeks, like tears. It flails then and will not settle. flinching from even those who wish it well. And the breath of it! The wind snakes through the streets, in the gaps beneath doorways, through window-frames and down chimneys; in the spaces between cloth and flesh and all the way to the heart where it chills a person, stiffens their bones and hardens their mind.

Everyone knows winter babies will not live until spring, that they have not the fight in them, but this is summer. Ruby's going now is wrong.

There be those as say that Frank has brought this on himself, from twice marrying someone from out of town. Though I counted Ruby as a friend, I cannot speak against them.

At first light Frank is out as usual on the boats. 'How else is a man to feed himself?' he says. 'How else is he to live?' No-one says he is wrong. We none of us think him cruel. We are practical people, after all. We are fisherfolk.

Diaspora
Neil Lawrence

For my father.

The man with huge whiskers is talking loudly, it wakes me. He pulls his face into wide shapes as if it will help with understanding. By my side little Hannah stirs like a mouse. She wrinkles her face at the smell that has built up in the compartment. It is inevitable, packed into the bowels of a passenger liner as we are, *Farshtunken*. Hannah wipes sopping hair off her forehead. It is *Shvitzing* like a Turkish Bath down here.

This is the new start for our new century.

'Lazarus?' the whiskered attendant asks. He pronounces my surname as if learning a new language. I want to sigh but nod energetically. I wonder if my husband, who took this journey months ago, experienced these moments of frustration. To my left, my mother-in-law, Bubbe Gittel, stirs.

'Liverpool,' he says.

I know this word. This means we have finished the first part of our journey. That we are far from Gdansk. Even further from our shtetl in Novograd-Volynski. The shipping company have performed this *Mitzvah* for us. I stretch to let my bones click into place and get up. I help sleepy-headed Hannah before I tickle her. She giggles.

Now we restart the clock of our lives.

We climb steep stairs, pausing at each deck. We make way for the better dressed and the better smelling. We linger in a rat-tail line until we are allowed up top.

The sky of England is the same grey as home. The smell on the wind is bad eggs and salt. Bubbe Gittel draws her thin coat closer to her, hands gripping at its edges. She is staring at the dock workers below. They are schlepping large containers. Is she expecting trouble like the neighbours in Novograd? Is she remembering the Russian army?

'Sara?' she says to me.

'New home to come,' I tell her.

Her face is tight. 'Noo Yok,' she says, a well recited prayer.

Hannah hugs me tight.

We are led across an unstable bridge onto a floating platform. We are on a long walkway. In the distance I see three overwhelming buildings go up into the sky like Towers of Babel. Zalman Levi, a remote cousin on my Zayde's side, approaches with a smile and takes hold of Hannah's hand. Hannah wriggles her fingers free and says, 'Your beard has gone white.'

'Your words are rude,' Zalman Levi says to my daughter. But he smiles.

We are led towards the buildings. They are the colour of bones stripped clean then left to rot. I follow the rows of windows upwards and there are too many to count. Near the very top is a large clock, so big it can be seen from far away. My head is tipped far back with the effort of looking up. But I am not finished yet.

At the very top are four rounded domes with two statues of birds. One has wings thrust behind its back. It eyes me suspiciously. The other looks ready to take flight, with a snaking neck that cranes forward. In its leering beak is the twisted spine of a rodent. *Come here dirty Jew. Let me play with you.* I imagine my neck gripped in its jaw. The pressure of Cossack teeth, like the time I was shoved against the wall. I remember the rotting breath and the caked-in staleness as he reached for the drawstring of his military breeches.

Hannah is tugging for me to move on. She is shrinking into my skirt. Despite the coldness of the wind, my insides are on fire and my head is in the past.

Noach screeches through the lanes, tattered and grimy. The soldiers burn Noach's house. We are the chosen people. Chosen for death.

We are led past the predatory birds who look the colour of filth, of drek. And I am back in the past again.

I trip over Mrs. Friedman in the rush to get away. They have tossed her away, broken.

We are led between pillars grand enough for a temple and then inside. Hannah's mouth is wide open. In this large concourse there are Jews, but also others with unwashed clothes like ours, many of them have hair the colour of flames.

We join the back of a long line. I keep Hannah's hand held tight and check Gittel is still with us. Her lips are moving though she says nothing out loud. I recognise the shape of her words. *I enjoin upon you this day, to love the L-rd your G-d and to serve Him with all your heart and with all your soul, I will give rain for your land at the proper time.*

My mouth is moving also. I am rehearsing words I learned from the ticket master in Gdansk. They are needed for the next stage of our journey.

My name is Sara Lazarus. I am twenty-seven years old and I am a seamstress. I meet my husband Moishe Lazarus. He is with my Aunt, Sofia Cukierman, at the Oceanic Hotel. We travel to New York. I carry $100.

At the front of our line is an official. For the first time since Gdansk my hands shake. Hannah looks up at me, eyes wide, and I force myself to relax. I join Bubbe in prayer.

The line moves slowly. We are behind an old scholar who sighs deeply. A goyshe man in the next queue points his pipe at the Hakam and bursts into laughter. The woman next to him silences his giggle with a slap. Serve the lobbus right.

When we get to the front of the line the official creases his forehead like a furrowed field. I repeat my English sentences and this seems to satisfy him. He bends over a form and fills it in. He hands it to me and points in the direction of the exit at the far end of the hall. But he gives no ticket.

'New Yok,' I say.

'No,' he says.

I know that word.

'Gdansk,' I say. 'To New Yok.'

He shakes his head. 'Liverpool.' He says. 'No more ticket.'

I grab Hannah's hand so tight she moans. I think of my Moishe. Does he know about this? I have granite in my mouth. I was coached by a man who knew I would never get to America. I think of my precious Menorah, and the family ornaments I had to sell. I clench my teeth to stop my eyes from stinging.

The official has a sad smile. He has had this conversation before. 'Sorry,' he says, 'Mrs. Lawrence.'

Lawrence? He makes my surname sounds as foreign as him. He points towards the queue and shrugs. I gather Hannah and Gittel and guide them towards our new land. My life in G-d's hands.

Out on the street I shiver against the squalling weather. Other Jews are being rounded up by a man speaking Yiddish. 'Oceanic Hotel? Travel to New York?' he shouts out. Gittel starts towards them and I grab her arm.

Gittel looks confused. 'Are we not going, Sara?' she asks.

Hannah looks up, reads my expression. 'Grandma, we stay here,' she says. Her voice is strong. No longer a curled-up mouse. I stroke her hair proudly. *Klaybing nachus.*

Gittel looks confused. 'Noo Yok?' she asks.

Hannah shakes her head like a sage. She points to the pavement. 'The pavement is not gold. Only in New York is it gold. This is Liverpool,' she tells her Bubbe.

The Oceanic group move off. Zalman Levi is trailing at the end. He turns around, tugs at his beard and runs back.

'Aren't you coming?'

'No tickets,' I say, astonished at how calm I sound. 'Our tickets only bring us to here, to Liverpool. If you see Moishe in New York, tell him – please, tell him.'

He nods, pats Hannah's head and runs after the disappearing group.

We are now the only Jews left on the street. Ahead of us, on the wide road, horses pull carts and passenger coaches. Hannah absently clicks her tongue in time with the hooves. Men pass us in well-made coats. Their hats have short round brims. This is just another work day to them. They look cleaner than us, smell cleaner than us. Their faces look fatter too. I close my eyes, wait for the flecks of spit to hit me. But when I open them again, no one is scowling. One woman even smiles.

Two fellows dressed in heavy frockcoats emerge from a passageway and walk with the swaggering steps of policemen. On their heads they have oval shaped helmets. Hannah giggles. 'Muter, they wear black shiny eggs,' she says. I shush her, feeling sick in case she is understood.

I look up at the sky. That bird is still looking at me, the bird of death. All the strength goes from my legs. And now the policemen are heading for us. I swallow. The metallic taste of the docks still in my mouth. The smell of Novograd is back in my nose.

In the market square a policeman listens to local troublemakers. I watch from the safety of a passageway, not daring to move into the open. They hold Rebbe Yitzchak's arms pinned behind his back.

They say, 'He blessed other Jews by praying to the devil…' They say, 'He sacrificed our children to their g-d…' They say, 'He used fire to burn out their insides for eating at Zhiddy meals…'

They carry him off. I never see him again.

I am ready – but these Liverpool policemen, they pass us by. One gives a gentle nod.

I breathe out my fear, maybe for the first time in years. My shoulders drop into a restful position. My neck gives out a relieved crack.

In the distance there are two new figures. One is bent under an invisible weight, but her head bobs enthusiastically at the man she is talking to. She is wearing the same length skirt as me and Gittel. The man is skinny like a pole and gives a familiar lurch of his right leg. But his pace is faster than I have seen before. It cannot be. Hannah tracks them both with intense eyes.

The stone in my stomach lifts. It moves towards my heart which is opening wide. I look at the sky. There is a patch of blue. It makes the Liverpool birds look burnished. One has its chest thrust out proudly. And it is a flower in the beak of the other, not a decaying rodent. They are fierce angels who protect the city.

What *mazel* to be stranded here.

The old woman and tall fellow have increased their pace. Bubbe Gittel gives a strangled cry. It cannot be, but it is. Hannah's chuckle is uncertain. Her father waves. I let go her hand, but she doesn't run towards him, so well-schooled in fear. My fear.

I prepare to dare to let go.

Sea Change
Diana Powell

There are voices here.

They hum around her head as she walks down the path to the sea, or when she wanders outside the storm-blown wall.

They have been here since the first day she came – a foolish place to come to, with houses and people half-gone. But those that were left had taken her in, when others had shut doors in her face.

The sea was something else she heard from the start.

As she walked west, it had played in the corner of her eye. A frittering of blue on the horizon, a simmering cupful, when she mounted a rise.

But now she knew its sound, its smell, the feel of it.

She must know it all the time, she must know everything about it, the villagers told her.

It was how they lived.

Voices meant ghosts. 'Who are you?' she asked them, as she walked between the white stones, marking the way. She liked these stones, white from the Atlantic weather, sun-glazed in the heat of the day. She followed them at night, too, when they guided her, rime-struck by the moon. The voices were louder then, but there was still no answer. They carried on with their conversations, about the potato crop, and the kale, and the fishing. No different from the people she lived amongst now. Her people, they had somehow become.

When she first arrived, they gave her the cottage at the topmost corner of the hamlet, the one bedded in those outer walls, the one nearest the sea. A single room, a hearth, a pallet for lying on. Home. The windows were no more than clefts out of the stone. To keep out the gales, they told her. But there was still a snatch of sea, if she stood on tiptoe, if she crooked her neck.

She wanted more.

'You'll have too much of it soon enough,' Sarah, her closest neighbour, said.

But she didn't, she hadn't. It became everything to her, too.

They gave her a day or two to settle, and brought her more furnishings from those who had gone. Then they woke her early, and said 'This way'.

47

Her first walk between the stones, out towards the blue. And there it was beneath her – the water, caught in a bay, then stretched towards the sky.

Y Gesail the bay was called. *Armpit,* they translated. And yes, that made sense – how it curved in tightly, between the body of the coast, and the arm of the headland.

She saw boats moored to metal rings, burrowed into the cliff-sides. The men unfastened them and rowed away.

Boats, fishing, the deeper waters weren't for women, it seemed; they must stay on the shore. But there was still plenty to do.

'Watch, and follow us,' Sarah said. So she did, and soon learnt to stand in the shallows, with a net, or line, to catch crabs; how to sort and clean the fish, when the boats came in; gather seaweed for fertiliser and food. The women talked as they worked, or sang. Sometimes they forgot she couldn't understand their language, and fell into an up-and-down lilting, jarred by snagged-in-the-throat sounds. They taught her some of the words. The name of the place Maes-y-Mynydd. *Bore da. Diolch. Môr,* the sea, the one she liked best.

Her favourite task was to watch for the shoals coming in. That was when the sea was too rough for the boats. But they must still fish; fish was food, fish was money at the market. She would sit on the furthest promontory, the crook of the arm, where there was nothing but water and sky, and scan the surface for a shadow, for birds diving in the waves, or skimming along them. And when she saw it, she must run back, waving her arms, so that the men could sling a rope from one side of the cliffs to the other, then pull a baited line across, to hook the incoming fish. They praised her then, saying her eyes were the sharpest of all the women. But she was the youngest, wasn't she?

Before long, the weather was too bad even for line-catching.

'The worst for a dozen years,' the old man told them.

They shook their heads. Soon, another family packed up and left. And a month later, another.

Old Dafydd told other things, too, sitting at his hearth on the long winter nights, made longer by the lack of work. Stories of the sea, that held her close in the fug of the fire. Of the strange creatures that dwelled beneath its surface. Selkies, he called them, half-seal, half human.

'Fishermen are trapped by their beauty, and fall under their spells.'

And of a kingdom lost beneath the sea, to the north and west.

'Once upon a time, it was a place of singing and dancing. Music. Listen carefully and you will hear the chiming of the bells. You can see the land sometimes, on a fine day.'

She looked for it from the edge of the headland, where she went every day, no matter that the fishing had ceased. And yes, when the sky was clear, she could see a shape above the horizon. But she thought it no more than a distant range of mountains pushing out into the sea. Seals were real enough. They were something else that spoke to her, especially when she sang to them. There was something human about them, the way they looked at her, their heads above the water, but selkies? No, she thought not. There was no sign of them that she could see.

There were other stories in old Dafydd's words – tales of the people who used to live in Maes-y-Mynydd, who made the houses in the beginning.

'A strange kind of people,' he said, 'with different ways of worshipping, ways that their lordships down in the valley didn't like. 'Friends' they called themselves, but the townsfolk became their enemies, confiscating their possessions, poisoning the well, to drive them away. The women were said to be witches.'

She had been called a witch, once. After her husband died, even though she had nursed him, giving him the potions that she had always made. It was then that she made her way west.

Was it their voices that she heard?

The winter went on, 'the worst for three decades'. Other families departed, until only she, the old man, and her neighbours remained.

Morgan, Sarah's husband, shook his head over each day's catch. The two women sat on the beach, cleaning the few fish he brought in. It didn't take long. Dog fish, again. The mackerel were too small to be of any use. Afterwards, they walked down into the town with their cutlets and tried to sell them in the market. There were so many other women doing the same, with bigger, better fish.

'We'll go in the Spring,' Sarah said. 'Dafydd will be dead by then. There's no point staying any longer. We'll head east, to one of the towns. Morgan will find work in the mines or the steelworks. We should have done it a long time ago, like the others.'

There had been letters back at first, telling of new homes where there was piped water – no need for a well; where they could buy food from the shops, with the good money the men were earning. The letters stopped after a while. None of them mentioned missing the sea.

'Where will you go?' Sarah asked her.

She would miss the sea. This thing she had not known, then came to love. She could look at it endlessly. She could smell it, taste it, feel it in her bones. 'It will have my bones one day,' she thought. She wanted it to have her bones. She didn't want to return to the east, to the towns. She had learnt what towns could do. But there was no more 'west' to go.

And yes, the old man did not survive the winter. They buried him in the churchyard down in the town.

'There is no place for graves here,' Morgan said. She knew he was wrong.

There was no fishing anymore. The potatoes blackened in the ground. The shellfish had retreated into depths, along with the seals, the selkies. Morgan sold his boat, ready for their departure.

'You can come with us,' Sarah offered, but she said no. She would stay a while longer, follow them later, maybe.

'Thank you. *Diolch*. Thank you for everything.'

Afterwards, she wandered through the empty houses. 'Take anything you need,' they had said. But what was there to take? A right-footed boot, a saucepan with a hole in it. The rank of fish. The emptiness of life. Besides, she had everything she wanted in her own place, for a while longer, at least. How long would it be before these houses joined the others in a heap of stones? Would hers survive another storm? She would have to leave. She could not stay on her own. But where could she go?

Each day, she walks along the path to the sea, then scours the beach for what it can give her. Seaweed, to make into bread, as the women taught her. A crab or two, if she is lucky. Nettles, in the wall, on the way back.

Afterwards, she sits on the cliff-top, looking outwards. If the day is clear, she can see the line between the sea and the sky. She can make out clouds and waves. And between them she sees a shadow of a land.

High mountains to the northwest, she thinks. Or the old man's magical kingdom. Somewhere people are happy all the time, where gold lies strewn on the floor. A kind of paradise across the sea.

If there was such a place, she would go to it. But it is not real, is it? Still, she could walk towards it. Yes, perhaps that was what she should do – walk into the water. For a few brave minutes she might swim beneath the waves, become like the selkies. And then, lungs, heart, flesh will surrender. She will have what she wanted for her bones.

After all, what else is left for her? Nothing, except that sea.

The voices tell her where to go. They have grown louder, now that she is alone. Louder, and stronger as she follows the white path, or wanders outside the wall. This is where the graves are, she is sure now. The graves of those others who were here before. This is where their ghosts are.

Or maybe it is the words of the old man, listened to afresh, taking shape in the full light of day, away from the lull of his voice, the warmth of the fire. Or talk in the marketplace, that she had paid no attention to, now settling in her mind. It doesn't matter where the telling comes from, though she likes to think it is the ghosts.

'We crossed the sea,' they tell her. 'Far further than Ireland, far further than the mythical shore, but another kind of paradise. America. A place where Liberty greets you. We began new lives there. You can begin a new life there, too.'

She has had new lives before. This was a new life, and it had come to nothing. But this time will be different, perhaps. She will listen to the ghosts.

She will sell all the goods that are left, even the one boot, and the leaking saucepan, walk to Fishguard and take the boat to Liverpool, with all the money she has made. Then she will cross the Atlantic to America. On the journey, she will know the sea at its best and its worst. When she gets to the other side, she will stay near the ocean. She will have to look east, then, rather than west. But it doesn't matter. It is still the same water. It is hers, forever.

Casting the Stones
Cathy Lennon

The party went out of the garden gate and set off along the duckboards. Captain Chivers, upright and dapper at its head, swung the hamper with studied ease. Behind him, twirling a parasol, skirts brushing the marram grass, her mother. To the casual observer, Esme thought, they looked like husband and wife. With little Charlotte dancing between them, chattering away beneath the yells of the three boys who whipped at each other with towels. Esme lagged behind, head sagging like an abandoned marionette.

As soon as the roof of a pale green beach hut appeared, the boys plunged ahead. Dumping their towels, they veered towards the sea. Its lazy frills whispered against the deserted sweep of sand that sheltered in the arms of two discreet headlands. At one end a crumbling slipway slanted down from a derelict cottage.

'You and Charlotte first, Esme.' Mother opened the beach hut door then turned her profile to stretch and inhale. The movement lifted her neat bosom and showed off her graceful arms. 'Captain Chivers and I can wait.' She smiled at him with the corner of her mouth. Esme looked at the open door and stepped back. Purple smudges appeared in her vision and her heart began to pound. She turned away, as if regarding the boys, scrapping like seagulls at the water's edge.

'Esme!' the woman snapped, as she bundled Charlotte inside. Captain Chivers cleared his throat and began rolling up his sleeves.

'Our Esme strikes me as more of a beachcomber than a bather, what?'

The girl turned towards him and he winked. She fixed him and her mother with a stare. 'My daddy is going to teach me how to swim. When he gets back.'

Mother bent to the hamper and retrieved a wine bottle. 'Your manners this holiday leave a great deal to be desired, Esme. At this rate, I shan't shed a single tear when you go back to school.'

Esme's gaze remained steady, but her cheeks reddened. Captain Chivers rubbed his chin and nodded. 'Off you trot then.'

Sweating in her summer dress Esme scuffed away from the hut, away from the Chivers boys and their blabbering sister. Without a breeze to lift the wisps of hair from her face, they clung to her skin like the seaweed on the slipway at low tide.

She had seen this beach in the moonlight, seen it without its foam-laced skirts: disturbing, leached of colour, and dotted with dead crabs. She'd nearly stood on a seagull carcass, lying bundled and twisted, beak open.

She remembered seeing Mrs Chivers sleeping on the sofa in the billiard room. Her stays and hair had been loose and her mouth had gaped, drooling. Around her the air hung fetid, yet oddly sweet. She had thought of Mrs Chivers when she'd seen the dead bird last night.

By her toe something glinted emerald in the sun. She crouched and lifted the nugget of sea glass. Slowly she rolled it between her finger and thumb, then pocketed it quickly and began to sift the sand. Bareheaded under the glare, she prospected for jewels.

'What are you doing?' The youngest Chivers boy's navy woollen bathing suit dripped onto her sleeve. She ignored him. 'Can I help?'

She hunched her shoulder against him, but he squatted beside her and began sweeping the ground with a stick.

'Go away.'

He dropped the stick and began to sift the sand as she did. 'Can I come with you to your hiding place tonight?'

She picked up the discarded twig and stabbed the sand. 'No.'

'Please, Esme. They always find me first and you're always the winner. Let me come with you.' His fingers touched something and he pulled up a blunted shard of brown beer bottle. Esme reached for it and he tugged it back.

'If you give me the stone, Billy, I'll let you come. But not tonight. Tomorrow.'

The others were shouting for him in the distance and his attention wavered. 'Alright.' He handed her the glass and scrambled away.

Esme rubbed her two gems on her dress and held them up to the sky. Daddy had told her the story of the magical jewels that the Japanese Sea God used to command the tides. He'd made her say the names: *kanju* for ebb, *manju* for flow. When the Sea God dipped the flow jewel in the waters, they would surge forward, inundating all in their path. When he dipped the ebb jewel, those same surging waves would retreat. Daddy taught her lots of words and stories from his travels, but she liked his Japanese ones the best. She loved the dragons. She pictured them slithering and swirling in the skies, belching out flames that chased away their enemies. When he had pretended to be fierce like a dragon, daddy's moustache had waggled and she had laughed. 'Esme-chan,' he said, and caught her to his chest. She had lain there, snuggled into him, right beside his heartbeat.

A gull screamed. The sky mocked her, empty and blue. Over by the beach hut her mother and Captain Chivers lay side by side, like the stone effigies in the church they'd visited yesterday. She could see that they were talking, her mother's lips curving into smiles. She picked up the stick again and thrust it into the sand, twisting it deeper, clutching it so that a splinter drove into her hand.

Tonight, after supper, when Mrs Chivers lay indisposed and the children ran riot and Captain Chivers drank brandy with Mama, she would return to the beach. With no one but the moon for company, she would dip the green jewel into the sea and summon the flow tide – she would squeeze under the beach hut again. Only this time, when Mama and Captain Chivers arrived, she wouldn't hold her breath. She wouldn't stay, sick and scared, beneath the floor while her mother gasped and moaned, and the hot tears rolled into her ears. She would plant the green jewel and wriggle away. She would flee the beach hut, the garden and the house and climb up onto the headland to watch.

The waters would bulge, and the waves would race, and she would see the flow tide engulf them all. And only when her father's dragon danced and swooped triumphant in the night sky, only then would she reach into her pocket and pull out the ebb stone. Pull it out and hurl it into the waters, sure that when they receded all would be revealed: the slime, the carcasses, and the sands swept clean.

'Esme!' Her mother's shrill call carried across the bay. The other children clustered around the hamper. She kissed the stones and put them in her pocket. Slowly, under the weight of the faultless sky, she made her way back to the hut. The stones clicked as she went; as if they were just ordinary pebbles.

Herr Dressler
Eoghan Hughes

I had left the Alma at closing time and was stumbling along the breakwater the first night I saw the light at sea. That itself was not unusual – Harwich is after all a port town – but it was not the unblinking brightness directed towards the lighthouse that caught my attention, but the silhouette of a man on the shingle, down at the water's edge.

This dreary stretch of the Tendring doesn't receive many visitors, so thinking the poor man either lost or drunk, I shouted down, 'Excuse me!' but it made no difference. He either didn't hear, or simply wanted to be left alone. He continued with his peculiar vigil, waving towards the beam, ignoring the spray and the swell.

I watched him for several minutes, before the wind whipped up and brought me to my senses. I turned homeward. Not everyone wants the half-cut assistance of an overeager local.

A few weeks later I was again wandering through the streets after closing time, beyond the lighthouse towards the sea wall, although by then I'd forgotten about the man on the shore. It was a clear night and the air was crisp and I could see into the distance in every direction. Lost in thought, it was only when I heard a low moan that I stopped. There it was again. That light, brighter this time and closer to the docks than before. It looked as though it was hovering and was no further than a mile out. But I had seen no ships in daylight. There had been no tanker or ferry appearing on the horizon that afternoon. He was there too. That man, standing by a groyne, though now more animated in his movements, as if he were caught by some great excitement.

This was too strange for me to ignore, and I started down towards him. If it was a ship, it would be some time before it docked and he would freeze waiting for it to arrive through the early hours. The very least I could do was to see him home.

As I drew close, I could see a speck of orange light from a cigarette drooping from his mouth, which revealed the soft features of a middle-aged man. Unshaven and windswept, clothed in a threadbare suit, I guessed he had spent many days and hours standing there. He was muttering to himself, although I couldn't tell what language it was. His accent could have been Dutch or German, but he spoke so quietly, none of the words were clear.

He hadn't noticed my arrival and I was about to reach out and place an arm on his shoulder, when he simply vanished. Not like a magic trick in a cloud of smoke, but as suddenly and as definitely as though a lamp had been switched off. I stopped dead and looked out. The light out at sea was gone too. There were no footprints on the sand except my own.

Of course, no one believed me, not my friends, not my family. I had been drinking too much, not sleeping enough, they said, and I would have agreed with them, had I not been so sure of myself. I needed to prove what I had seen and, in the days, and nights that followed, I spent hours looking for clues. For a cigarette butt or a bit of clothing, for one of the green-lit and bobbing buoys out of place, but there was nothing to be found, nor had the fishermen and the dockers, usually so alert to even the smallest of nautical comings and goings, seen anything.

A couple of years later I saw him again – this time on the front page of the Harwich Standard. I recognised him immediately; the picture showed the same middle-aged man, cigarette at an angle, unshaven, though now with a hand brought to his forehead and avoiding the camera's gaze. He was clutching a portrait of a woman and two children. Above, in block capitals, the headline read: '70TH ANNIVERSARY OF MV HOFFNUNG TRAGEDY'.

I read every word. It seemed that the man, Herr Dressler, originally from Hamburg, had in a previous role as an envoy, been able to secure safe passage for his young family to join him from Rotterdam, ahead of the German advance. Harwich is not a big place and during that time Herr Dressler became something of a well-known figure in the area. For as the ship drew closer, he had taken himself down to the shore, where he could be seen, staring out to sea, awaiting its arrival.

The crossing had been fraught and by the time they reached the Essex coast a deep mist had risen and slowed their approach. Gunners from the redoubt, inexperienced boys drafted straight from school, mistook their merchant ship, which was carrying nearly 600 Jewish refugees, for a destroyer and panicked, firing at it. Despite the odds and the conditions, their arms were steady and their aim direct.

I put the paper down and stared out along the promenade to the rising horizon, distinguished only by differing textures of grey. In the distance above, a circle of gulls stalked a juddering trawler. What I had witnessed now suddenly made sense.

And so, Herr Dressler still waits, or at least a memory of him does, on the shore, seventy years on. Watching for a ship that will never come, carrying his family, who will never arrive.

Hingland
Pauline Walker

Constance was only just beginning to enjoy the voyage. The seasickness that had plagued her for the first two weeks of the journey had been left behind like the churning tail of water that followed the ship as it sailed towards England. Her eyes were shiny now and her ashy pallor restored to vibrant brown. She clung to the railing on the upper deck of the SS *Orbita* with one hand and with the other held onto her straw hat as the wind tried to whip it from her head. She grinned and nudged at Jackson's hand squeezing her waist.

'Stop it Jackson, people is watching we.'

'Don't mind the people them. No-one cares about a man kissing his wife.'

Jackson squashed her body against his and she let go of the railing and her hat.

'Jackson, my hat!'

Her laughter followed him as he dodged passengers to chase the skipping hat rising and dipping along the deck. She caught up with him and wrapped her arms around his neck, not worrying about what the other passengers thought as she kissed him; he had saved her one good hat.

'Cut that out, man,' said Winston. 'We're gettin' together a few boys to play dominoes.'

'Another time, man.'

'No, you go, Jackson. You've had no fun looking after me all this time. Go.'

'You sure?'

'I will enjoy the fresh air and look for Hingland on the horizon.'

'Well you're going to stay there for another seven days before you see any Hinglish land,' he teased.

'I will stay right here, rooted to the spot, until I see the Queen herself waving at me. Go on.'

'Maybe you should go lie down for a little while, Connie? Your eyes are over bright.'

'Go on Jackson Richards. I am well.'

Jackson followed Winston to the mess, several decks down and next to the loud and smelly engine room. The mess was crammed with rows of tables and dining benches fixed to the floor, unchanged from when it was a war ship. They joined a table of Jamaicans, Trinidadians and Barbadians. Jackson shook hands with the men he'd only nodded at for the last two weeks. He should be with Connie, in their cabin, rocking to the rhythm of the swell beneath them. A glass of rum was pushed his way. He sat down, gathering and mixing up the dominoes, and took the cigarette offered to him and stuck it between his lips. To spice up the games they promised each winner things they would get in Hingland: a week's wages, a gallon of paraffin, a pair of silk stockings.

'Where you getting silk stockings from?' he asked Winston.

'My brother livin' in London, in a place call Brixton. He has plenty things from the war under his bed. All Englishwomen wear stockings.'

Jackson won the promise of three pairs. During the fourth game a man with a crumpled suit and grimy shirt entered the mess. He spotted the noisy group slapping down dominoes and headed for them.

'Me can join?' He eyed the bottle of rum.

'I don't have any more clean shirt to give to you boys,' said Winston.

'Come on, man. You can't help a brother to reach Hingland without shame?'

'I'll make you a deal, Sylvester. Let's go one on one and I will lend you a clean shirt if you beat me, but if I beat you, you must wash all of mine for the rest of the week.'

Everyone laughed, except for Sylvester who kissed his teeth in annoyance.

'Here, man.' Winston handed him a glass of rum and moved aside, making space for him on the bench.

Up on the top deck, Constance watched thick black smoke billowing out of the ship's funnel, darkening the clouds for a few seconds before it drifted away. The voyage hadn't quite been the second honeymoon they'd thought it would be, but Jackson had never left her side, until now, and she had never felt so adored.

She had gone as often as she could down to Kingston Harbour to look at the ships, and imagine herself sailing away to Hingland, and that's where she'd first seen him, negotiating a price for his baskets of under-ripe bananas with the representative from the All Banana Company. If she'd stayed in Jamaica, she knew her life would continue its slide into endless servitude: cooking, cleaning and washing for the lawmakers in Kingston for one shilling a week and a tiny room next to the kitchen, forced to eat their leftovers spotted with saliva. After they married she improved her position to personal maid to the Governor-General's wife, where she got two shillings a week and saved as much money as she could, earning extra as a seamstress in the evenings, while Jackson travelled around Jamaica for a year working as a fruit and vegetable picker, driver, mechanic, carpenter. They saved enough to buy one single fare of £28.10s and half of another one. Jackson's father was persuaded to sell two cows to make up the shortfall.

She dreamt about the better life that was waiting for them in Hingland –

a house with three bedrooms, plenty of room for children, a plot of land where I can grow...
but they say it's cold in England, you can't grow things like bananas and mangoes and coconuts
and coffee... Jackson will work as a mechanic, I'll train as a nurse send money home to Mom
and save hard and after a year or two we'll have plenty money to go back home build our own
house in Linstead...

'Constance? You're looking much better.'

Constance smiled at Eunice, Winston's wife. 'I feeling like my ole self again.'

'Where is Jackson?'

'Playing dominoes with your Winston.'

'Winston likes to win. I hope Jackson doesn't promise him something he can't afford to give up.'

'He won't risk our future.'

'I wish Winston was so sensible, he's already lost one of his good shirts to a stowaway.'

'Shush, decks have ears.'

'Winston says they will make things worse for us, if they get caught. The authorities will send us all back because of them.'

'How can they send us back when they've invited us? We have our papers and everything, we're coming to work, to build up Hingland and build up ourselves too.'

Later, in their tiny cabin, crammed into the single bunk, Constance asked Jackson again, 'You scared?'

'About what?'

'About what's going to happen to us when we get there?'

'Man is not scared about what's going to happen.'

Her finger circled his chin.

'They say it's cold in Hingland.'

'We can keep each other warm.'

'What if...?'

'No more worryin'. I have a surprise waiting for you when we reach.'

'What is it?'

'Me can't tell you now, a surprise is a surprise, you'll have to wait.'

Early one morning, Jackson and Constance were woken by someone banging on their door. 'Hingland, Hingland. Come look 'pon de mother country.'

They forgot jacket and shawl and joined a packed upper deck, pushing their way towards the bow to see the swell of the land filling the horizon through the drizzle. The huddle shivered as a sharp wind rushed their faces and whipped their words of awe away towards the coastline. The captain's voice boomed from the loudspeaker 'England ahoy'. Nerves and elation surged through Jackson and Constance and they clung to each other as the throng listed to the left.

There was a rush as passengers returned to their cabins, bumping into each other, tripping on the stairs, a rising timbre of excited chatter swirling along the corridors.

Jackson whistled, trying to remember the boys' calypso tune from last night. Constance brushed Jackson's jacket and helped him put it on, smoothing it down over his shoulders. Jackson fixed her flimsy straw hat with a hatpin he'd traded from Eunice, giving her a clean shirt. The foghorn blared, signalling that they were approaching land. Jackson flung open the cabin door and they squeezed themselves into the jostling mass of bodies crawling along the corridor.

They finally disembarked an hour later.

'This way, Sir, Madam.'

Constance was amazed to hear the white man in the porter's uniform calling them sir and madam. They were shepherded out of the rain and bustled into the customs hall full of men, a handful of women, suitcases, boxes and barrel-sized straw baskets tied up with string.

The chatter swelled and abated and swelled again as those nearest the front of the hall relayed the words of welcome from the government, a man from the Ministry of Labour, to those at the back. 'We welcome you to Britain and Liverpool. We are glad that you, our colonial brothers and sisters, have answered the call of the motherland to help return Britain to the prosperity of its former, glorious times. You will be taken from here to a number of boarding houses where you will have food and a bed for the night. Tomorrow you will be taken to the labour exchange where work will be found for you...' The speech was interrupted by the group of stowaways nearest the exit, who began to cheer and wave their battered trilbies. The man from the ministry raised his bowler to salute them. '...But first please queue for your identity cards and ration books.'

Jackson spotted Winston and Eunice near the front of the line. 'Come.' He clasped Constance's hand. 'Hey man, Winston.' He shouted and pushed through the melee.

'You reach, Jackson,' said Winston. 'You ready?'

'Yeah, man.' Jackson turned to Constance. 'This is my surprise. We are going to London.'

'London?'

'Winston's brother have a house in London, plenty room for all of we.'

'The Queen lives in London, Buckingham Palace.' Constance's skin prickled with goose bumps. She had a letter of recommendation from the Governor-General's wife. 'How long will it take to get there?'

'By this time tomorrow.'

*

They caught the last train. Bodies and luggage crammed themselves into every carriage. Constance sat on Jackson's lap as thirteen people squashed themselves into the six-seater carriage. She snuggled into Jackson and soon the warmth of his thighs seeped into her legs and she dozed... a house without windows...ripe mangoes falling and smashing on hard ground, sunny flesh crushed, sweet fragrance turned rancid. The train jolted and she woke. *London?* She peered through the window, searching for the familiar constellation of stars, but the darkness was opaque. She felt an echo of the rising and falling of the sea that had caused her sea sickness as the train continued to jolt. A torrent of rain battered the window, startling her. She gazed at Jackson, breathing easy in his sleep. A chill slowly suffused her skin.

The Dowager Duchess of Berwick-upon-Tweed May or May Not be Bottling It
Rob Walton

She hated the Dowager bit, and she no longer particularly cared for the Duchess part, but she had not yet decided what to do about any of it. Charles, the Duke, had died in his sleep eighteen months previously, and she had now been called upon to launch an ocean liner on the River Tyne.

It was only on the railway journey to the city that she found out the ship would not then be sailing across to New York, as she had first expected. According to Mr Parsons, there was another year's worth of work, fitting it all out. It did not even have the funnels or propellers at this time, so would hardly be joining the race for the Blue Riband for fastest Atlantic crossing. She could not personally understand why people gave so much of their energies to the need to do things quickly. Surely there was an argument to slow down and look around you. What was that poem in the book Maud had sent her, about having no time to stand and stare? She stared across the river where the crowds were growing on both banks, and then she looked out towards the sea. She could not actually see it from here, but knowing it was nearby always improved her mood and clarified her thinking.

As so often happened at these events, unctuous officials checked everything with her over and over again: how she should say the few words somebody else had prepared for her, then gently launch the beribboned bottle towards the bows of the ship. She looked at the bottle attached to the new rope, and looked at the little man who had pointed to it and explained again, as though he doubted her abilities to take all this in and perform the task correctly. Well, she would prove him absolutely right.

She waited patiently while the Tyneside Artillery Band played three compositions and the Chairman of the ship-owners made a speech. This was followed by another given by a man from the shipbuilders, and finally the Mayor said a few words, before handing over to her to officially launch the RMS *Great Northern*.

She cleared her throat and thought of the meaning of Dowager. It was concerned with being a widow with a title or a property derived from her late husband. From where exactly did he get it? From the toil of people like those lining the riverbank today. From people like her, running and organising the show while he smoked cigars and drank brandy in panelled rooms where women were not allowed. Now it was time for her to have a drink and time to raise a toast. Over the last few months she had sensed something in the air of this great country, and she was not sure if she could properly be part of it. But she could at least try.

The launch of the Titanic had been receiving all the attention lately, but she thought she might be able to change that ever so slightly.

She was not sure how well her voice carried, and whether everybody could hear her, but they could certainly see what she was doing and she knew it would appear in the local and national newspapers. She could tell they heard her when she spoke of the Queens of the Tyne, but not whether they registered when she went on to say,

'To the women of Tyneside in the homes they have built, to the families they have forged and to the furnaces of their hearts and their minds.'

With that, she took hold of the bottle and opened it, taking care to ensure it did not leave her hand and head for the bows on its rope. She took the most delicate sip she could manage without a glass to hand. She raised the bottle high, shouted 'To the Queens of the Tyne,' and waited for the newspaper reporters and photographers to do their best.

The Wreck of the *Kyllikki*
Cindy George

Sea coal just washes up on the beach and no one knows where it comes from. I mean, they do, it's just that everyone thinks something different. Some think the North Sea pukes up the grains and crumbs of coal from underwater seams, its cold grey heart rejecting anything that might hint of warmth. Others just gesture up the coast, where a busy colliery once used seawater to float out the dust from the chunks and lumps that made up their living. Either way, you don't see so much of it now.

You don't hear the sea coal men either. Once, they'd be round every week, before the mines and the steelworks shut down, in the days when foreign cargo ships still skirted the town's spiteful rocks. 'Sea coal, sea coal,' they'd bellow over and over, in voices that sounded like they might fill their rollup cigarettes with the stuff. The bags didn't look heavy, after all it was only dust. But they'd been on the beach since before light, filling those bags to sell to families who were still poor, but had a bit more than they did. Sometimes I'd get sent out with a shilling. It was hard to get them to notice me. I was small and unremarkable in those days, and I kept back, scared of their black-lined faces. I couldn't shout like them and I was easy to not notice. They always noticed the shilling, though, and the extra penny to put the sack in our back yard.

Sometimes there'd be a big storm, and the sea coal men would be out on the beach before the wind died down. The coal would be thick in heaps, then, making the grey sand sparkle darkly, covering the eternal dogshit and broken glass, and the night's stranded jellyfish. I could have painted a picture of those mornings and hung it in a gallery, and nobody would say 'Well, that's only the beach.' When it was like that, people would know, they'd send their kids out with whatever bags and sacks they had. A lively enough storm could keep a household going till the next one, if they had enough kids and enough bags. It burned just as nicely as the proper stuff, once you packed it in a parcel of newspaper and tucked in the ends tight.

If the storm was far out at sea, the first you heard of it might be the flares that called out the lifeboat. A bang. Then another bang. Then people, putting their coats on, tying their cheap chiffon headscarves, shuffling out of their houses. The front doors straight onto the pavement, bang bang bang. It was the best free show in town when the lifeboat set out. Grimly gleeful, old people – younger than I am now – would quietly group to watch without enjoyment as disaster played out far on their horizon. Their faces never changed. It was awful, it was lucky, it was for the best. All the same.

This time, the flare was on a cold afternoon that smelled of damp and medicine. I'd been given somebody's old broken vanity case to play with, and I was sticking scraps of wallpaper onto its plastic face because it wasn't pretty enough. I must have been slow to get ready when I heard the flares, because I remember being pulled out of the house by the sleeve of my second-hand yellow coat, still clutching the empty vanity case.

There was already a small crowd by the sea wall. The sea was grey, but not wild. It didn't look as though it could just take you and never give you back. No-one else was looking at the sea, what was interesting about the sea? They were looking at the lifeboat house. A few children ran onto the slipway, danced about, daring the lifeboat to come and run them over, then darted back behind their mothers. I never dared go on the slipway, even on a fine quiet day, because it was dangerous. I wasn't allowed to ask why.

The show was beginning. Men, unrecognisable in new plastic lifejackets – their fathers would have only had wax to keep the water out. I wished I had a plastic jacket to make people like and admire me. They didn't look at the crowd as they brought the painted wooden boat out of its shed and into the storm. They had probably stood and watched the boat go out themselves once. Or maybe not. None of the onlookers today looked like future plastic heroes.

At a distance that could have been arms-length or could have been miles, was a ship that looked like a toy. It was wrong. Even I could see that it wasn't straight in the water. Someone said it was going to sink, and I felt sick. For the first time, it occurred to me to think about the men in that ship, human people who shouted and smoked cigarettes, and if the ship sank to the bottom of the sea, they would be dead. Next time I was at the beach, they would come and get me, take hold of me by the arms and legs and carry me off to be dead with them in their shipwreck. That big container of people was going to turn into a real live dead shipwreck right in front of me. I couldn't stop it, so it must be my fault.

I wondered if the drowned men would be kind to me as I walked down the slipway and into the sea. No-one tried to stop me, or even seemed to notice that I'd followed the lifeboat into the waves. Close up, the foam looked a bit like the thick beige condensed milk you squirted out of a tube. Once I was underwater, though, it was all just bright and cold and exhilarating, just like the time I was allowed to sing on the stage at assembly and some people clapped.

I thought someone talked to me under the water, but I expect I imagined that bit. It turned out afterwards that I had mumps and should probably have been to the doctor, so I was probably seeing all sorts of things that weren't real.

It was the sea coal man who pulled me out, but I didn't know until they told me. I didn't know him with the lines washed off his face, holding my dripping vanity case instead of his sack of coal. When I went back to school, the kids were all saying he was my dad and calling me Coal Bastard. I knew that was wrong, though, because I didn't have a dad, so they were just stupid.

There wasn't a happy ending. There wasn't an ending at all. Nothing changed, not till the year the ship started to fall apart in the water. Then flakes of metal started to wash up on the beach. They'd get into the sea coal and shoot out of the fire with a bang. Bang. Bang. As if the ship that drowned still wanted to be noticed. Lots of people moved into the posh new council estate with central heating and nearly everyone stopped buying the noisy sea coal.

I grew up. It took a lot of singing and shouting, and a long time, longer than some sailors ever lived. Everyone in this town knows how long that is.

The Professor's Daughter
Barbara Renel

Her dad locks the booth and gives her the key. 'Sort the clock, will you?' He heads off, pausing to look back and shouts 'Don't be late!' She watches until he disappears. It had been a bad morning. The sky overcast, her dad's mood matching the weather. He'll be off for a beer or two. Earlier, she had arranged neat rows of seats in front of the booth but had spent much of the morning drying them off after each rain burst. There had been some soggy families, unimpressed, unenthusiastic. Most punters seemed to be taking refuge in the pavilion and the safety of the slot machines in the arcade further along the pier. She moves the wooden hands.

Next Performance
Today
2:30

The Punch and Judy booth, with its red and white stripes and promises of slapstick, swazzles, and audience participation is in the kiddies' corner of the fair alongside the toys-2-ride, the mini planes, the candyfloss stall. When she was younger, she was proud to be the daughter of the Professor, the Punchman. But now she wants leathers and DMs, she wants to be part of the big rides, the fairground proper. Holding onto the pole at the back of the dodgems, swinging from car to car. She'd like that.

She fastens her hood under her chin and wanders along the pier. Music is playing, but the big wheel, the swing ride, the whip, all deserted. Goldfish in plastic bags have been abandoned. Rifles at the shooting range lie idle, the ducks continuing their circular journey without fear of being shot at. But, come the night, when the rain catches the lights, when the smell of burgers and hotdogs mixes with the grease from the rides, the girls will be there. The girls, arm in arm, with their lipstick and petticoats, with their giggling and flirting, with their stilettos stuck in the decking, with their screaming in competition with the waves below, pretending to be afraid. And the boys will be there too. The boys, loud, confident with drink, the boys will be there to rescue the girls.

She leaves the pier and goes down the steps onto the beach. She takes off her shoes. The sand is coarse and yellow, the sort that sticks to your soles, stains your feet. She walks past the solitary giant 99 ice cream cone. The seafood kiosk is shut. The donkeys are using it as a windbreak, trying to find some shelter from the grey drizzle. She loves the donkeys.

'Hello, Daisy.' She puts her arms around the animal's neck and buries her face in its wet mane. 'Miserable. I know.' She hugs each donkey in turn. 'There Alice. Won't rain forever, Dixie. Cheer up, Charlie.' She strokes their noses, pats their rumps, nods at their owner.

The boy is sitting in a deckchair, leaning forward on his fists, his hood pulled tight round his face.

'You look really fed up,' she says.

He looks up at her. 'No one wants a deckchair.'

'I do.' She bends down and kisses him.

The boy gets up and wipes his face. 'You're all wet.'

'Been to see the donkeys. Where's my deckchair then?'

There's a heap of blue and white folded deckchairs by the hut. The boy picks one up.

'How long do you think it'll take me to put it up?'

She shrugs. 'No idea.'

He stands it up, twists one bit then another, puts the chair on the ground, adjusts the seating angle and gestures to her to sit.

'Should I be impressed?' She sits down tucking her shoes under the seat. He adjusts his own deckchair and they sit side by side in the rain, looking out to sea. They have been seeing each other for a couple of weeks. He's not local. The deckchairs are a holiday job. She likes him a lot. He's not like the boys she's used to. He kisses her gently and hasn't tried anything else.

A seagull screams. She looks over at the pier.

'You know, if you lean on the rails at the far end of the pier, it's like you're on a big ship far out at sea. You can feel the wind, taste the salt, hear the waves. It's like you're going to America or somewhere. Maybe I'll go to America one day. I'd like that. Do you want to have sex with me?'

The seagull screams again.

'I'm not supposed to leave the deckchairs unattended.'

'If you don't want to…'

'No. I mean, yes.'

Inside the hut, he stacks deckchairs against the door 'just in case'. They kiss, he fondles her breasts. The floor is gritty with sand. He pulls at a tarpaulin, 'keeps the rain off the deckchairs when they're outside,' and lays it out. She lies down, takes off her jeans and knickers.

'Have you done this before?' she asks.

'Of course.' He drops his jeans and falls on top of her. He's in a rush and struggles to push his way inside her and then it's over. He rolls off and lies on his back. She turns to look at him. He looks as pleased as punch. The top of her legs are sticky and she sits up, finds a tissue in her jacket pocket. He gets up and she watches as he pulls up his jeans and re-fastens them.

'Have you got time for a cup of tea? I'll treat you.' He kisses the top of her head.

'I thought you couldn't leave the deckchairs.'

'It'll be alright.'

He buys her tea at the beach café. Hawaiian music is playing. It's still raining. They sit in the big bay window looking out to sea. She stirs sugar into her cup.

'How long you staying?'

'End of August. I'm going on holiday, then to university in October. Leeds. What about you?'

'I live here.' She looks across to the dots of people toing and froing along the pier. 'I've left school. I don't have to go back.' She blows on her tea. 'Maybe I'll see if there's work at the holiday camp along the coast.' She sees the donkeys being led away. 'Or maybe I'll get a job in a donkey sanctuary. I'd like that.'

Granmama's Paradise
Holland Magee

When I was little, I slurred my syllables together. It drove my grandma crazy. She would put her face level with mine and say 'grandma' like she was giving an army command. Then I would stick my tongue out and repeat 'gamama.' She rolled her eyes, put a toothpick in her mouth and then said it again 'grandma!' and I would respond with 'grama.' After many frustrating hours and countless toothpicks, she finally settled on 'granmama.' It was the only thing I ever saw her change.

Not that my granmama was a boring person by any definition. Her feistiness was practically triggered by noise and her house was so cluttered it became the only tourist attraction in Cyprus Bay, Florida.

Granmama woke up to her chickens squawking at the hour she had trained them to years prior. She slapped on her light-wash jeans that were rolled up a quarter inch, and her raggedy blue sweatshirt. Her hair was a stagnant Afro with strands of grey peeking out from beneath the black and her fingernails were the appropriate length for her job as a fisherwoman. Or rather, a fisherwoman and a granmama. I was usually woken by the clanking of pans making scrambled eggs and fish sticks, but stayed between my bedsheets until her commanding call for breakfast. We ate fast, then she would hand me the gear and walk to the boat. She would position her squatty legs square to the dock, lift me up and place my little body on the piece of wood she made into my seat, slap her knees and say, 'We're gonna catch some big ones today, Lilly!'

The boat was her paradise. The water was her paradise. Me and the water and her was her paradise. She never told me, but it's not hard to tell when somebody is in her paradise. She has a certain ease, a vision that nobody else can see that pauses her life for a blissful moment, takes away every bruise on her soul and every skeleton in her bag. My granmama's only indication she saw the vision, however, was the faintest smile. The littlest rise at the corners of her mouth. Some days the smile would not come and others it was all she could understand, her very own language.

Smiley days were quite predictable, though, they only accompanied complete silence. If our neighbour, Gerald, spoke to her as we set up the boat, the ride that followed would entail Granmama's relentless gripes. Gerald was never rude to us, however, he had only one persona of pure jolliness.

'Are y'all gonna catch a lot today?' he called one day as we loaded the nets.

Granmama was feisty enough to glare at the man for a few seconds, but not impolite. She responded plainly, 'Yes, we are.'

'Well that's good, I know y'all will do great! This shore needs you guys!'

He gave a smile that made Granmama's look like a frown, to which she responded with a flat face and nod. Then angrily pulled the engine and we were off to a non-smiley ride.

She snatched a toothpick from the bottomless stash in her pocket and wrapped her mouth around it like a cigarette. 'All men want is your body. Never forget that! I know Gerald seems nice and whatnot, but it's all a ploy to get into your pants!' She began to fidget, her mouth moved sharply, lips slimy from the repetitive licking of her tongue and dancing of her toothpick. I understood her shakiness to be anger, given how every time she shook I received an earload of harsh commands, but now I realize her shaking indicated fear. Indecisive fear, that is towards any one person and towards every person at once.

I watched her nervous body carefully, then asked, 'Granmama, what was my mama's name?'

She turned her head slowly and looked at me with a solemn expression. Neither of us said a word for the rest of the ride.

We caught sixteen fish that day. Piled them into the old bucket and tied the boat to the dock, all the while Gerald swung his grandson on their squeaky swing set. Gerald was only five years shy of my grandmama but his grandson, Marcus, was a year older than me. Marcus shared his grandfather's jolly spirit, with wavy hair the colour of wet sand and eyes bluer than the shore after a rain.

He lived with his mother, Melody, and her father. Out of the three talkative residents in that house, Granmama only ever spoke to Melody for longer than a curt greeting. They were rather friendly friends, her and Melody. Rocked together on our back porch for hours while I searched for seashells and dived into the water head-first, imitating a dolphin.

My skin had a film of salt water as I ran up to the women one particularly musky afternoon. I begged 'Can Marcus and I go swimming? I really want him to!'

Melody's face turned apologetic. 'Well, maybe, if…'

'No, you may not, young lady!' Granmama interrupted her harshly. I hung my head, disappointed but not surprised. The only time I ever spoke to Marcus was followed by Granmama swooping me into her arms and checking my skin for bruises.

Nevertheless, butterflies fluttered in my stomach when I saw Marcus' sandy hair. He had a certain ease in his disposition, a dead giveaway he lived in his paradise. His ocean-blue eyes filled my thoughts as I tried to go to sleep, making my cheeks blush and my heart race.

One night, in the middle of my sandy-haired fantasies, I heard a weeping sound. I followed the sound upstairs and found Granmama crouched at her bedside. She was picking through a little wooden box of seashells while tears ran down her cheeks. I rushed to her side and wrapped my arms around her.

She took a deep breath as if she had just realized she could breathe and met my eyes. 'Your mama's name was Daisy. Daisy Rae Howard.' Granmama swallowed, looked down. 'She was the… she was an amazing woman. I loved her more than the sun and stars,' she smiled as she flipped through her memories. 'I used to tell her that every night. But I don't know if she knew how much I loved her, really and truly. I wish I could hug her and kiss her and tell her I loved her more than life itself. And,' her soaked eyes turned to me, 'I love you more than life itself. Never forget that. Anything you do, any choice you make, it's your choice. Don't think about me whenever you make a choice. I'll love you no matter what you choose. Always, always, always.'

My little body held hers tighter than it ever had before. I laid my head on her bony shoulder and glanced down at her arm. It had never occurred to me I'd only seen Granmama in her blue sweatshirt, I'd never seen her forearm. It was wrinkly, as expected, but it had lines. Light lines that paralleled each other, protruding themselves from the darker flesh.

I asked 'Granmama, what's on your arm?'

Her face dropped, she quickly grabbed a towel and covered her tank top. Slowly but not harshly, she said, 'Baby, they're scars. Sometimes people get very sad and they, they give themselves scars.' No words were said for the rest of the night, only two skinny bodies locked together with an ease.

*

When I was a teenager, I shopped for a living. It drove my granmama crazy. She would say, 'When you catch as much fish as money you spend, we'll be richer than the queen!' But I didn't spend money, I only looked, I window shopped, browsed all the antique stores and strip malls in walking distance.

I was sifting through trinkets one afternoon when I noticed two men eyeing me. They had their backs angled toward each other. Shifting to the left, I only heard snippets. 'Is that the Howard girl? I think it is.' 'Who?' 'The one whose mom offed herself 'cause her baby daddy ran away.'

My world went black. I had an urge to vomit and kick and scream but my body was limp, disabled. The walk home is hazy, but when I arrived, I sprinted to Granmama's arms hysterically.

She rocked me like a baby, ran her appropriately cut fingernails through my braids. Kissed my forehead and let me feel her lips, sticky from the tears she wept. No words were said, they didn't need to be. I knew she felt horrible for not telling me, I knew it was the reason for the lines on her arms, I knew she would go back and kiss my mama's forehead a million times if she had the chance. We just sat and cried for hours. It was the last time I ever cried with my granmama.

Three months later she passed away. I held her hand as she watched the waves from her window.

Just me and the water and her.

I stayed in my bed for days after the funeral, weeping and thinking. One afternoon, in the middle of my frizzy-haired fantasies, I heard a scuffle sound. Followed the scuffle to the front door and found Marcus, setting down a fruit basket on my doorstep.

'Hi! Um, I heard what happened and I'm so sorry. I want you to know if there's anything I can do, I–' He went on for a while, gave the same spiel as every sorry soul who came to the funeral. His fingers tackled each other and sweat poked from above his eyebrows. I stared at him plainly, didn't say a word. Just listened to his voice. It was shakier than I imagined but still deep and clear like sea water. I gave him a slight nod that told him to leave, not because I wanted him to but because Granmama would never allow us to talk.

I closed the door and walked back to my bedsheets. Sat down and remembered the hours I had spent fantasizing about the sandy-haired boy. Then, when I looked up, I found a little wooden box of seashells perched on my dresser.

My granmama's words played in my head.

Don't think about me whenever you make a choice. I'll love you no matter what you choose.

A tear dripped from my eye before my hand could sweep it away.

I grabbed my shoes, walked out the house, and knocked on Marcus' door. He opened it and I kissed him. A salty-lipped, teary-eyed, picture-perfect kiss. Ran my fingers through his sandy hair and looked into his ocean-blue eyes.

*

I'm an adult and I'm sure it would drive my granmama crazy. I married the man she never let me speak to and my fingernails exceed the appropriate length. But I'm happy. I'm so happy. And I know she always desired my happiness far more than she feared men. I don't fear men. I don't fear anything. I start the boat every morning and I lift my granbabies into it and I smile to the wind and I put sand on my face, and I smell the salt water. I'm in my own paradise and the only vision I see is my granmama.

The Answer My Friend...
Paul Foy

It might be that the day takes you down to the beach with your book and wraparound sunglasses, your Beats and that blast-from-the-past playlist that you made when you realised that loss is all about finding again. A song comes to you, but you need more than converted analogue to help you navigate your own depths. There's stuff in there, way in there, teasing at your present, whispers of memories like little fish scrabbling at a dropped morsel of food that bobs in defiance of direction.

It might be that you stay on later than you planned, as the wind challenges your digital noise. 'Fight back and damage your ears,' it tells you, and there on your own you learn that the wind can laugh, and why wouldn't it? It laughs like your granny did when she told you stories that didn't sound true but must have been – after all, it was Gran doing the telling.

A stronger gust of wind, sand that makes your eyes water, and you are here with her again, taking shelter between the anti-tank blocks and pillboxes. She's muttering because she can't get her match to stay lit. You never thought it was strange that she rolled her own cigarettes; you were told never to ask where Grandpa was. Once she gets it lit, the end of her rollie glowing, she'll tell you about the day the weather stopped the slaughter.

'The enemy came in on boats, shooting at our boys on the beaches, while our brave soldiers shot back at the figures jumping through the oncoming waves, yet not a single bullet hit its target. Why? I will tell you why. Because the wind was so strong that day, even stronger than today,' – and even stronger than the wind now, which in this chosen present feels like the same wind from all those years ago – 'and that wind had put up with enough of their nonsense and blew all the bullets up into the air to swirl away, off out to sea to sink harmlessly to the bottom.

'But was that enough? No. The order was given and out came the bayonets, men terrorised by their own determination to mutilate and kill. The men in the water, up to their waists, then their knees, then speeding forward as their feet raced against the surf.

'On the beach our men stood ready, terrified, but staying where they stood, wanting to drop their rifles and run, because they had loved ones waiting at home.

'It was at that moment that the waves whipped up into whirlpools and everyone stopped as the air roared a warning. It spun around them, all of them, friends and enemies alike, nudging them on the shoulder, sneaking in behind and thumping them on the back, grabbing their helmets and messing up their hair. And do you know what it did then?'

You don't answer, but your gasping face says that you can't wait to hear more. Your granny's words are blowing about above your head and you're hanging on to every single one of them for fear that this moment will get away from you.

'It was so sick and fed up that it blew the faces right off the men.'

'Oh Gran, that sounds a bit silly.'

'As silly as men trying to kill other men they didn't even know?'

'So, it blew their faces off? Can the wind really do that?'

'It's the wind, it can do what it likes.'

You draw that wind, the very same one, right into your lungs, holding it there, savouring the strength of it.

'So, then the men had to scramble all over the beach and in the water to try and find their own face, but that's easier said than done. It's a strange but true fact that the face we find the hardest to recognise is our own. We could pass it in the street and not give it a second thought.'

'What did the men do?' you ask. You put your hand to your cheek to make sure your face is staying right where it should. You think of all the muscles and blood vessels exposed to the elements; all those nerves exposed to a world more intense than your skin had ever let on.

'They did the only thing they could do – they picked up any face they could find and put it on.'

'But what about the sand? Wouldn't it get under their skin?'

'They were so glad to get a face back that I doubt they even noticed. And after all the faces were put in place – and they fitted surprisingly well, even though they weren't the right ones – nobody was sure who was enemy and who was friend. They looked at each other, and when one man looked at another who was meant to be his enemy, what he saw was the face of his best friend, the young man he'd gone to school with, and learned how to grow up with, and trained in the army with, knowing that one day they might die together. And even though he had his bayonet pointing right at the beating heart of a man he had been trained to kill, the love that was in his own heart wouldn't allow him to do. And it wasn't just one man this happened to, it happened to them all. In those few moments mortal enemies became closer than men had ever been before because they knew how close they had come to doing the worst thing possible they could do to another man – end his life and stop him appreciating the beauty of the sand, and the sea with its waves and its fish and its seaweed and shells, the beauty of the wind that teased the sea so that it sent up little waves to try and catch it. But everyone knows, you can't catch the wind.'

You put your open hands up now and feel the wind playing through your fingers, and you close them slowly, knowing that you are grasping at nothing. Except when you open them again and stretch them wide you can feel that the wind is still there. As long as you don't try to force it, it will still be there, teasing you, tempting you to grasp at it. It's then that something puts the idea into your head to go down to the surf and wet your hands, and when you've done that you hold them up and realise that your hands are beginning to sparkle as grains of sand fly to them and stick to them.

Perhaps you should leave now, but you don't. You stay and watch as your hands dry and the grains begin to fall off. Not all of them, but when you leave the beach you will have to clap your hands together before you can drive your car, wash your hands before you have your tea. You can't eat with dirty fingernails, can you now? What would your gran have said? You'll be all cleaned up and presentable. Not to worry though, you can always come back and have your hair mussed up by the breeze, the way your granny used to do when she'd say, 'Come on, my little soldier. Time to head back.' And you'd say, 'But I thought you don't like soldiers?'

'Do you see those waves out there?' she'd ask, pointing with her knobbly finger. 'Fighting to rise in a rough sea? That's the fight you are fighting.'

'But won't I lose my face if I start fighting?'

Your granny smiles. 'For that fight the face you have will do just fine.' Then she'd rub your head even harder, mess your hair up even more, then tells you you'd better brush it before going home. 'You can't go about looking like that.'

Now it's time to leave the beach, and you walk with the wind behind you. The temptation is there, to look back into it, to see where it leads back to, but try that and all you'll get is sand in your eyes. Instead you squat down and pick up piece of sea glass, a shard of broken bottle that has been rubbed so smooth you can no longer make out what the raised letters on it say. You would wish for more, but it'll have to do that you can feel the shapes with your fingers. And when you get home, you'll put it in the big bowl with others that you've been collecting since long, long ago. You and your granny. Together.

Turquoise
Sheila Lockhart

Every morning after breakfast Ibrahim walked down to the perimeter fence to look at the sea. Today a bitter wind cut across the wasteland round the camp, whipping up the shreds of plastic caught in the scrub. Ibrahim held his thin coat close. The sea beyond, unreachable but ever present, was dark grey, all churned up. White birds wheeled and screeched restlessly above the waves. He had been living by the sea for nearly a year now and had seen it in all its moods. He liked it when it was cold and rough like this. It calmed him.

He remembered his first sight of the sea last year. They had been travelling in the lorry for days, only stopping at night to rest and eat. It was hot and dusty, and they were all exhausted. The drivers didn't talk much, and Ibrahim never knew quite where they were, so it was a shock when the lorry suddenly stopped, and they were told to get out and take their things. As Ibrahim climbed out, clutching his rucksack and bed roll, it looked just like all their other stops, a rubbish strewn road surrounded by rocks and sand, but there was a shimmering brilliance in the air around them, and a strange smell, fresh and clean. He sniffed and screwed up his eyes against the brightness. He became aware of a sound he had never heard before, a rhythmic rushing, a bit like the rustle of palm fronds in the wind, or like the women sweeping the dead leaves in their yards at home. It came from beyond the gravel bank beside the road. He and the other boys grabbed their things and scrambled up, eager for their first sight of the sea, the final barrier between them and Europe. They had been talking about it for days. Ibrahim had seen pictures of it in his school book and on TV, but nothing prepared him for the reality.

The vastness made him gasp. It stretched as far as the eye could see, from the long dark strip of coastline that was the edge of Africa, all the way to the distant sky. The colour of the water, such a deep blue, reminded him of his mother's turquoise necklace, the one she had sold to help pay for his place on the lorry. Small waves were breaking with a lazy rhythm onto the sand, running back into the sea as if afraid of getting caught, leaving a delicate white mesh of foam behind them. Some of the bolder boys were already running down the beach, laughing and whooping, pulling off their shoes and T-shirts and splashing into the water. Ibrahim hesitated. He had heard terrible stories of this sea. It had claimed the lives of a whole family from a village not far from his own, who had made this same journey a few months before. There were no deep rivers where he came from and he'd never learned to swim. But the turquoise water was irresistible, and he was hot and badly in need of a bathe. He took his trainers off and walked down to the water, feeling the hot sand beneath his feet. As he stepped into the water, he caught his breath. He hadn't expected it to be so cold. He walked in deeper, the waves lapping up against his legs, a little higher with each step, making his flesh tingle. The sand oozed between his toes. He looked down into the clear water and saw light sparkling through the ripples, making patterns on the bottom, while tiny silver fishes darted round his legs. He cupped his hands and lifted them up to the sky, letting the water trickle back into the sea through his fingers, as he said a prayer of thanks, just as he remembered his father doing after the first rains filled the creek behind their house. He knew you couldn't drink sea water because of the salt, but it looked so pure he couldn't resist tasting it. He spat the salty water out and pulled a face. The other boys laughed and splashed him until he was wet all over. Then he plunged in, abandoning himself to the thrill of the cold water on his hot skin.

It was three days before the boat came to take them to Europe. They were happy days for Ibrahim. He loved it there on the beach. There was something soothing about the voice of the sea, like a lullaby. He went to sleep with its song in his head and when he woke it was still there. Every morning he walked down into the water and looked to the north, to his future, wondering what destiny was waiting for him over the horizon. Small boats moved slowly up and down the coast, and further out larger ships could be seen going about their business. Men came in a vehicle each evening with food and fresh water, but otherwise no one bothered them. At night he and his companions would eat the food and talk about their plans.

At last they were on the boat: Ibrahim was too afraid to talk to his companions any more, but being crammed so close together at least gave some warmth and reassurance. The weather was calm, but even so, the waves were bigger when they got further out to sea, and most of them were sick. Some of the younger boys cried, the older ones comforting them as best they could, struggling with limited English or French where they had no common language. When dawn came, they couldn't see any land, just water and sky in every direction. Ibrahim prayed that he wouldn't drown in this empty desert of water.

When the Italian patrol boat intercepted them, the boys cheered and cried with relief. They were happy to be taken to the camp.

But Ibrahim was still here. The officials didn't believe he was only fifteen. They needed to make further investigations. Lampedusa in the winter was bleak. The wind blew and sometimes it rained with a cold, hard rain. There was nothing much to do. Twice a week volunteers came to help them learn Italian, and new groups of refugees arrived with news from Africa, most of it bad. They weren't allowed to visit the town, for their own safety, they were told. There were guards at the gate to stop them going out. Each morning Ibrahim looked out through the chain link fence at the ever-changing sea and thought about Africa, and his home beyond the horizon. He had crossed the sea, believing in its promise of a better life on the far shore, and all he had found was disappointment. But today, as he watched the birds swooping and screaming in the wind, something in their wildness touched his spirit.

He would not give up hope.

TIME POEMS

Arrival
Valerie Bence

1
It starts by not sailing on a Thursday or Friday
        or the first Monday in April or the second in August,
Saturdays or Sundays are preferred, the 17th and 29th being especially
auspicious.
Don't step on board left foot first, wear green or carry a black bag
don't have red hair, be cross-eyed, clap
nor whistle unless you are the youngest on board or the ship's cook;
best not to be a woman, unless you're naked
        or about to give birth.
Never throw stones into the sea, leave a bowl or bucket
upside-down, have flowers on board nor cut hair or toenails
        once a ship has sailed. Sailors should sleep only on their backs.
Never let a bell ring – unless a watch bell – for it will ring for death.
It's useful to have a loved one's hair knitted into your sock,
to ensure your return to dry land, but don't let them wave you
goodbye…
Don't join a ship whose name ends in 'a', change a ship's name
after launch nor stick a knife in a mast
unless you are becalmed, as it will summon up the wind.
Never say thirteen, say twelve plus one; if there is a death on board
the sailmaker should stitch the body in sailcloth with thirteen stitches,
the last one through the nose, to make sure they are dead
and don't follow the ship.
Never say 'goodbye' 'drown' or 'pig' – especially not 'pig'
(use Gruff, Little Fella or Mr Dennis) but it is fine to say pig if you
have one tattooed upon a knee
        pig on knee, safety at sea;
In the galley, never cross knives on the table, stir tea with a knife or fork
or pass salt directly to another person – *pass the salt, pass sorrow*
never borrow a spoon, always eat fish from head to tail.
Egg shells must be broken into tiny pieces, to stop witches getting in.
        Pray for an albatross or dolphin to show the way to land,
never harm them, they carry the spirits of dead sailors.

2

A year she lived like this, newly married Mary
amongst such men who wore gold in their ears
to improve their eyesight or to pay Davy Jones if drowned at sea;
men who would never reach through the rungs of a ladder
to handle a flag – which would break the Holy Trinity...

A year to get there. If the world had been flat
they would surely have gone over the edge –
more dangerous then, they say
than becoming astronaut, blasting off the earth.
She would return without him, leaving seven babies behind.

A year's journey before she stood in dimity
and cotton lawn quite unfit for climate,
a little behind her husband in the small boat.
Soon she would have to disembark, blinded by the blue,
step on land as if she knew what she was doing.

Removing her too dainty shoes, she took his hand
jumped delicately onto bone dry sand.
They had God in their luggage;
but she may have had in her pocket the feather of a wren
killed on New Year's Day, for safe passage

Mary Williams, new wife of LMS Missionary John,
sailed to the South Seas on board the Harriet *1816-17*

In the Shadows, on the Shore, Leith

Jane Aldous

*The ancient port of Leith, close to Edinburgh
has always been a busy and colourful place full
of dark tales and ghosts. This is the voice of
one ghost bewildered at the sight of archaeologists
digging up her past*

Why do they always arrive
at such awkward times,
these people of the future
with dirt on their clothes,
carrying muckle tools?

One time they appeared
through a stone floor
as I was closing a man's eyes
in the plague hospital.

Another time I was kissing
a sailor on the sea wall
and they were on their knees
scratching at the mortar.

I see them mouthing words
I cannot hear, they come and go
fascinated by bits and pieces
of wood and stone and metal.

I'm such a cheeky besom, you know
but they never see me
or any of the sailors or stevedores,
dockers, merchants, beggars or women
working behind curtains and closed doors.

I've tried yelling in their ears,
blocking their way,
waving my cloak at them
to cause a stramash
but they just walk right through me.

The stories I could tell,
the characters I've seen,
from all the ships from every place,
the fights and curses, broken heids
and stolen purses,
all the peely-wally wretches
taken from below, cargoes
being loaded and unloaded,
wine and spirits, cattle, sheep,
not forgetting all the fond meetings
and departings while all around
lums are reeking.

Only the sea never changes,
always the same, in and out,
dark slaps against the harbour wall,
only the water knows
what's gone before
and what the future holds.

Of Gráinne Ni Mháile
Thomas Tyrrell

After Kate Garrett

To weave by hearth-fires she disdains,
Red locks cropped short against her skull,
The tameless oceans fill her brains,
Their cold salt spray, their fresh sweet rains,
Storms beat but cannot hole the hull.

Perched high while battle seethes below,
Red locks cropped short against her skull,
She sees the fight ebb to and fro,
Leaps down and deals the killing blow,
Storms beat but cannot hole the hull.

They raid the bays and prowl the shores,
Red locks cropped short against her skull,
Three galleys of a dozen oars
That fight for her and Connacht's cause,
Storms beat but cannot hole the hull.

Ringed round by brutal foes and mean,
Red locks cropped short against her skull,
She takes to sea – her true demesne –
Seeking redress from England's queen,
Storms beat but cannot hole the hull.

Fine silks and rubies gleaming bright,
Red locks cropped short against her skull,
Beyond their meddling courtiers' sight,
Two queens conspire by candlelight,
Storms beat but cannot hole the hull.

'My favour, grace and clemency,'
Red locks cropped short against your skull,
'I grant you, Gráinne Ni Mháile,
And I will see your son set free,'
Storms beat but cannot hole the hull.

Her family and lands secure,
Grey locks cropped short against her skull,
By no means gentle, chaste or pure,
She has the worldly-wise allure
Of those who struggle and endure,
Storms beat but never holed her hull.

A Conjuring Poem
Simon Whitfield

By primal life, dividing in the deep,
by giant shark and breaching ichthyosaur,
by nameless horror, dark in the abyss,
by rearing head, and ship-crunching jaw,
by loaded vessel, stately quinquireme,
by dragon ship, marauding from the fjords,
by leather curragh, questing caravel,
by sea-dog, moulding life to time and tide,
by sunny water, crystalline and still,
by donkey ride, by shading parasol,
by tanning body, seal-like on the shore,
by brochured holiday and package tour,
by monster wave, obliterating storm,
by poisoned fish and oil-polluted sand,
by drift of plastic flotsam, bobbing slow,
by dwindling shoal and scientific fear,
by these and more I conjure seven seas,
ancient, ageless,
extending a mantle round the world.

False Light
John Richardson

All is night fog. No moon or stars to tell
we have the lantern lure ready, lifted high

on poles by our barefoot women; dreamlike
they make a slow, silent, waltz down the beach.

The fog banks and drifts so thick at times they disappear.
But tonight, when it lifts, the lantern's false light ghosts out

beyond the distant breakers, from where we can hear
the laden creak and groan, the snap and crack

of fat sails stiffening. And glimpse, soft between banks,
the other lights bob and sway. A voice overlaps the waves,

By the mark – five! to swell the return, *See you no land?*
We wait, flat in the trap, for the answers calm,

No, only another's light, to know our false is true.
And wait; with the weight of drownings to be done.

Church Mary Sounds the Sea
Jenny Mitchell

Bend close. I'll say this once, tired from the weight of words.
You children have to know our strength –
a trick to walk on water.

Other slaves learnt fast to slip out of the hold, shaped by their blood,
chains silenced as if night placed hands to ears,
made crew and captain deaf.

Out on the deck, they looked towards the mount of light
beyond the waves where they were stolen.
Heard their names in distant trees.

Recalled themselves before the slavers
stripped men down to tears, pressed women into blood,
pulled apart the children's ribs.

All knew to pray for home, but how to kneel on a rough deck?
No gods in sullen sky, strange as the slavers' eyes.
How to dance for help on splintered feet,

outrun the whip's one aim – to push flames through the skin
till fear burned into veins, charred muscle, sinew, bone?
Yet children had to dance, despite their broken ribs,

hands held across their chests, to save hearts falling out.
They swayed close to the edge
to see the gods thought dead, curled in the waves.

Their mighty voices pulled down stars,
crashed against the ship till they heard clear commands.
The women acted first, climbed across the ledge to walk on foam.

Miraculous, men joined this calm parade, the children on their backs,
aimed at the mount they knew as home.
The sky grew pale. Rough surge became smooth sand.

They left the name of slave at sea for gulls to peck;
prayed under trees, picked fruit to gorge upon themselves again.
They longed for sleep as I do now the weight has gone.

Let go my hand. It's time to join the calm parade;
God knows, my work is done.
You've heard real strength lies just beneath our surface.

Napoleon
Nick Westerman

Napoleon
stares at his captor the sea, calm to the horizon, belying
its immensity and the insignificance of the dreams of one
small man wistful of the days when the fallen still stood, an
Armée grande indeed –

such insolence his captor cannot countenance and thus it
raises up, waves crashing, thundering on rocks and shore,
so alike, yet so dissimilar, to the sounds of cannon which
heralded victory, and defeat, and in this uproar the small
man has but one choice –

retreat.

Clearance
Christine Ritchie

Edging the darkness of the land, a gleam of grey
As, heavily, the white ship tears itself away.
Its ropes cast off. Set loose, sea-changed, it soars,
Wings spread, skims waves and westward sets its course.
Encouraged by the wind and tide
In close conspiracy, the gap grows wide
and wider still ...
Those left behind with urgency must climb the hill
Keeping close watch on shrinking sail and mast
To ward off what must surely come at last ...
Separation
     Emigration
          Isolation
               Desolation.

Scattered schist and gneiss gaze blindly out to sea,
Monochrome, imprinted still with memory.
Extinguished now the spark that could ignite those stones,
The force that gave identity, the fire of love that warmed our homes.
The great white ship, sea bird of black, black sorrow,
Our land left with the blackness of tomorrow,
The great white sheep, *an caora mor*
Mackay no more, Macleod no more, this land is ours no more,
And not one soul with power to give us aid.
And still the white ships ply their soulless trade.

How Women Came to Tristan da Cunha
Claire Booker

Too late for second chances,
they catch the island humpbacked on the sea line.

No room's been left for luxuries of love –
couplings will be made in single file, reeled off by number

blindly on the quay. Each woman hauls her sea-drunk limbs
along the black volcanic ledge,

sees the line of hats in hand, feels the burn
of strangers' glances – five wombs held out for filling,

five pairs of eyes already pouring on the mark –
past creels of crayfish, stinking skins, potato stacks piled high,

but does she dare to count her place ahead, or wait
until her sole comes in to dock beside his allocated boot?

Perhaps she lifts a modest eye, takes soundings of trouser seam,
belt buckle, frayed lapels. Checks the size of pupils

to rate his hunger for the night ahead,
whilst he sees in the wide horizon of her breasts, the colony

of sons they'll sow in the steaming furrow of the marriage bed –
same features rattling for generations in the island's rocky cup.

*Tristan da Cunha is a remote island in the south
Atlantic. Its tiny population descends from a
small garrison of 19th century British soldiers
and their 'mail order' brides.*

The Sinking of Mrs Margaret Brown
Michelle Penn

Silk elbow gloves. Yes, my diamonds and
snub me as new money, if you must. My hands
grasping other hands, women and children
in darkness. Surely you don't think
I've never held an oar, Quartermaster, and if
you don't turn this lifeboat around right now,
I'll shove you into the sea.

Margaret comes from the Latin for *pearl*.
Saint Margaret of Antioch escaped
from the innards of a dragon.

This dinner dress, beaded and blue, as royal
as you please, but no corset will keep me
from rowing. Bracelets an icy skin, water
clogged with deck chairs tossed
to those once flailing.

Here be dragons, as the old maps used to say.
Our ship twisted to a monster, reluctantly
expelling us from its guts. Tomorrow, I'll still hear
the cello, playing as the waves folded closed.

It's all the perfect story, a moment made for
Broadway: The Unsinkable Molly Brown.
Molly, a name I'd never use. From the Hebrew,
meaning bitter.

The Fisherman's Daughter
Claire Booker

My Dad was an artist with a needle –
woosh, woosh it would go, like Sunday rain
and I'd lie in bed listening to him
mending or making.

Nets came straight from the beach,
strung on a hook by our hearth, and he'd braid
right there, on a big old bedspread
between Mum's dresser and the pull-out table,

unhitching stories
until the room started rocking like a beamer
and I could smell the fish shoaling,
feel their weight as they pulled against the trawl,

bubbles breaking.
You could say I made a good catch, but
it was strange that first dawn with Bill lying
beside me: not a sound from downstairs,

as if the house had stopped breathing.
I still miss Dad's sure hands tightening the twine,
and his quiet ear for my life.
He was never one to tie on a smile,

but none of my worries
were too small to fling back and we'd sit for hours
looping and twisting the rows.
Dad called it cutting the holes out.

Once the little 'uns arrived, I knew
there'd be no hole big enough to wriggle through.
Fish don't know how to go backwards.
That's how it works.

When You Regret Wishing for Something Thrilling
Emma Lee

'Should be frightened, I should be frightened.'
She'd made a wish and let her bare hand hang
in sea spray. She heard the torpedo's clang
echo as she said, 'Should be more frightened.'
Lifeboats capsized. She thought about jumping.
She unhooked her skirt, a moment's practical act
to keep her vertigo at bay, and was swept
out, on the brink of death, ears still ringing.

Margaret woke under blankets on another boat.
Her dress was now a borrowed khaki greatcoat,
a uniform a woman was not entitled to wear.
She founded *Time and Tide* magazine to air
women's voices. Barred from the House of Lords
her portrait there still mutes her vocal cords.

*Margaret Haig-Thomas, Vicountess Rhondda,
founded* Time and Tide *magazine in 1920,
five years after surviving the sinking of the* Lusitania

The nth Wave
Math Jones

There's an old man who sits on a rock by the shore,
Says he's counting the waves coming in.
There's only so many, he says, and no more.
One day it will cease from its din.

I've counted them all since the day that I might,
And I've noted them down in my hand:
For every new wave that's rolled in on the bight
I've picked up a new grain of sand.

He showed me his fists, all crabby and vexed,
He showed me the fists of his son,
And as each new wave rolled over the next,
His load was enlargened by one.

There's only so many, says Dad, and he's right:
There's wisdom that none can deny.
And every new wave that rolls in on the bight,
Who'd want to miss it go by,

And who'd want to let it slip out of their hand,
To be tided away and forgot,
And so we mark each with a new grain of sand.
They showed me the size of their lot.

They gave me then each a disparaging look,
At my hands hanging loose by my side,
And made me regret all those moments forsook,
All those times washed away on the tide.

Then I wanted to count every wave till my last.
I picked up some grains from the beach,
And tried to recount all those waves of my past,
Found more than my numbers could reach,

Found more were forgotten, and more never known,
A mere two or three were mine to recall –
I gazed at the moments my memory had shown,
And let the remaining sand fall.

There's only so many, he says, and he's right:
One day it will cease from its din.
The few that I noticed roll in on the bight,
Those few are engrained in my skin.

But the rest are no more than the waves of the tide,
And are carried away on the turn,
So I let my hands hang loose at my side…

Frocks of Passage
Mandy Macdonald

1946, Wilcannia
Papyrus-white
baby smocks of smooth Egyptian cotton,
reed-pen strokes of purple pinstripes.
Grandfather's shirts outlived him
by a decade, dress fabric still rationed
in our corner of empire.

1954, Ballina
Even whiter, broderie anglaise
over layered explosion of organdie,
close-prisoning bodice,
pearly rivets down the back.
First communion, later let down
to modest knee-length for confirmation.
Liturgical creases never iron out.

1960, Sydney
Double circular skirt, jivey black cotton print:
Venice by night – sketchy gondolas,
barbershop mooring poles, water picked out
as flicks of white against the black.
I could have flown away in that one.
I almost did.

1966, SS Himalaya
Princess line, bias-cut,
not quite a shift dress – those would come
later, in a new hemisphere.
The print a blue and orange psychedelic maelstrom.
Navy mock-Chanel jacket on top.
A little suit to emigrate in.

2016, Aberdeen
Black lace, calf-length, sleeveless, square-necked,
smooth and narrow, flaring out
into a fluttery swirl for dancing.
Long stowed away, now shaken out
for my Scottish half-century.
The fiddles will brawl
through the pale midsummer night,
travelling the breathless patterns of the eightsome reel.

Overlord with Declan

Elizabeth Parker

I
At Arromanches, the Channel clouts concrete caissons,
gaps the line of Mulberry B
a mile from where Declan dips small hands
to stir up gobies,
net them for his plastic bucket.

Carapaces scooped clean of crabs
offer up minute reflections.
Declan strokes the pearl inlay
of an upturned fiddler
shaped like a stoop font,
gifts it to me.

We alter the angles of light, pop kelp bladders,
spin our fingers' heat through wefts of water.
The air that skims us is speckled with sea,
strokes rockpools, purring ripples
a mile inland from Iorys Hughes' triumph.

II
Declan has memorised the history
of this dark line lurking under shimmer.
Water flashes on his arm
as he prods the horizon,
his finger stubbing out a yacht.

Light streaks along his fingernail
as he speaks of Hughes, 1942,
sketching plans for the Mulberry harbours:
his pencil towing fine lines, ruling steel roads,
lightly shading six thousand tonne caissons.

The white space on Hughes' page is choppy today,
lurches to claim concrete
a mile from where shallows simper at our feet,
embroider our toes with foam.

III
Declan plucks a mermaid's purse,
pinches to pop the empty egg case
as he describes the mock-up in detail:
Hughes' drawings translated into paper boats,

floated in a bathtub on the *Queen Mary;*
Mountbatten bobbing the inky fleet
under his big fingers
to prove the prowess of the design;
newspaper pontoons leaking headlines –
The Times tinting bathwater
with battle updates.

Declan tries to deepen his voice:
'More waves please Lieutenant Grant.'
There is a dazzle on his lower lip
as he describes paper boats holding steady,
scudded by men's breath; a bath brush urging
a stronger pulse through the tub.

He pincers a trawler between index and thumb,
cuts to two years later:
paper models cargoed with light and air
transformed into tonnes of concrete,
steel, scuttled merchant ships
hefted by tugs across the Channel.

IV
We wade to our knees,
drag ourselves through the riptide.
Water rears, displays its weed
as Declan draws on air –
index finger hovering over the horizon,
tracing lost lines: pierheads, steel roadways
fanning toward the shore.

A child's finger to blot out a caisson;
one hand to hide the whole.

V
We are weak breakwaters,
taking hits for half an hour,
bearing the brunt
as water gathers its force
to shatter against us,
slinks back for the next strike;

the white space on Hughes' page
spending its strength on our skin;
frothing, blunting concrete corners,
blasting men's lines to dashes.

Sisterhood of the Seas
Alison Lock

We meet under the spire of St Nicolas's church
where the waterfront used to be.
We, three women, are cousins come to seek our roots
at the place where our great-grandparents wed.

We have certificates and documents to prove our blood
is theirs, though diluted in the brine, we share
a mix of Celtic heritage from a line
of wives and daughters of merchant sailor folk.

There's Margaret, eldest daughter, born 1873.
She's the one who stole the Orangeman's staff,
ran away with it across the fields. Years later,
she kept a candle in the window of her Groomsport home

to guide her sailor son ashore.
When asked if he might not see the sign, she'd say,
'If another mother's boy should follow the light, at least
he'd know himself be homeward bound.'

Then there's the tale of Ann, or was it Mary,
who took the helm to navigate the Straits of Moyle
when her husband took to drink?
Was he the Master Mariner or was she?

These are the wives, watchers, widows
of tides, keepers of the family.
As we, descendants, follow the family tree
of births, deaths, marriages, we raise a toast:

'To the women of the sailor-folk! You'll never be lost at sea.
In our safe harbour, your names are on our lips
as we retell the tales passed on to us,
through DNA your family's line secure.'

Half a Dozen Oranges
Mandy Macdonald

'*Hexi portokali, parakaló,*'
I was taught to say
by the Greek greengrocer in our outback town
when I was two.

In those days and those brindled hinterlands,
all greengrocers were Greek. Their eyes
contained voyages. Their deep voices growled
the rough kindness of Cyprus, Athens, Crete.

Later, in a new place,
parched and dust-whipped as the one before,
my mother prodded me proudly
to ask the new greengrocer for
half a dozen oranges.
Perhaps, she wondered,
he might teach me some more Greek.

'*Ochi, Kyria mou!*' His smile indulgent –
did he ruffle my hair, already dark and wild? –
'No, ma'am, I can't do that. You can hear
she's been taught by someone born in Greece.
Me, I'm from here. My father, now,
he was from Ithaca itself, made the odyssey
in 1893.'

Eighteen years on, at university,
I studied Homer in the original.
There is no word for oranges
in ancient Greek.

TIDE POEMS

The Arctic Diaries
Melissa Davies

The season was about community. Women contributed before the
catch and again when men returned with crates full of fat halibuts
that need to be prepared and packed. Forty boats and forty wives.
Boys didn't have their own rigs. First he needed a girl – providing
for a home was what drove them out when the west wind tore in.
Now they pray that they don't need luck to catch their dinner.

The Lookout Men

Her father's father was a lookout man on Løksøya,
the lookout island, watching the sea his whole life
with his back to his wife (who came from the agricultural
district of Helgeland but lost a brother to the sea
alongside sixty-eight Filipinos, three Swedes and a Brit).

Her father was a lookout man on Løksøya,
riding the low tide west he'd flicker out of sight
for long breathless minutes while he bound the boat
scrambled up goat tracks to watch the horizon. She felt
juniper spines needling through wool as she waited

for her father to lean his seawarped lean on the hill.
She knew his back by heart. Better than her mother
who didn't bother to look; that little patch of bare
earth was my doing, her mother would say,

I know the prickle of juniper on kneecaps
can hold my breath for the time one man
takes to reach that lookout peak and
I've seen more than they have
without once crossing that fjord.

Halibut

                    Fifty-six halibut tails.
Grotesque imitations of butterflies
tough as the nails pinning them down, ashy from winter rain
or spring frost. Some have split too far, begun to peel apart. Mermaids
cursed with legs, stumps of scales fringed by ochre flakes of meat
nodding on an easterly breeze.
The man who owns the hammer
                                        only comes here in summer.

A successful halibut catch
is always preceded by sex.
These petrified fish tails
are notches on a headboard
                              only
          it's the same woman every time.

One fin overlaps others, taking four nails to restrain cartilage
centimetres thick, petrified fingers contracted to form shadows
angular, sinister but still fragile
as skin off my palm.
                    I'm certain
this one proceeded the conception of a child.

In folklore the halibut is wise
a giver of sound advice

I'm told by the fisherman's wife who birthed four sons on this island
yet
          no tails hang from her walls.

Værøy

It's the weight of the mountain
forcing them to stay on the edge
with their soft flesh and felt clothes
houses built from trees
for the illusion of being solid.
A man chips tiles from the skin of cliffs

but it's the weight of the mountain
that shelters him from wind
from needles of salt
from sliding away with the bitter
tangles of kelp that crawl back
towards the water at high tide.

Stuck in the throat of the mountain
light belches east every spring
on the warm breath of the sea.
Wool here is woven close and heavy
to crack on a shin
snatch against an unshaven jaw

scoop winter rains or flakes of skrei,
herring and the round stones
of Mollbakken. Peripheral treasures.
Yolk of an eagle's egg slithers
down butts of gneiss while the shell
quivers in the salt grass glade.

The man lays down the chisel to see
Moskenøya calve his horizon
into opal halves. He imagines climbing.
Talons curling over the rim of the fin
calluses slip on smooth worn
stone beneath. He is the eagle.

Here on the peak he sees
the lost egg, the flash of sun
from a pair of fish carcasses swaying.
Here too the weight of the mountain
always draws their soft flesh and scales
to the bone edge.

Seaweed

So black against the snow
I can taste the summer *tang*.
Roll
          tiny bubbles
with the new shape
of my tongue.

Saliva rushes
to meet the salt
of their language.

Bird Wife

Otter belly brushes snow
filling wood gaps
with warm otter smell.
Daylight slips through glass weights
caught in plaster
breath makes the orb opaque
as she cries
          on the porch.

Otter in the eider house knows
language left with the fisherman.
Leaking from his tongue
silver strings shivered into buckets
guts from a spring catch.
Otter nesting in eider feathers,
bird wife wailing into storm wind.

Verticals
Kate Foley

Knobbly concrete crustaceans,
they hang on our sea walls,
built to withstand the flash
and rush of the sea,
to keep a miserly puddle awake
where small creatures can grow.

Displaced pebbles, fragile shells,
and small, soft bodies, clawed
or whiskered, plant their houses,
colonies of the dispossessed,
haggling over territory
and rent.

Yes. We do try, some of us,
while the giant sea, more macho
every year, roars with laughter
at our efforts, and Mother Earth,
with most to lose, cuddles our infant efforts
to her breast and sighs.

Constructions made to replicate the tidal
pools we are losing to our sea walls and the sea.

The Watchers
Elizabeth Parker

I
Of something far more deeply interfused
Whose dwelling is the light of setting suns
And the round ocean and the living air
And the blue sky, and in the mind of man.
(William Wordsworth, 'Lines Written a Few Miles above Tintern Abbey'.)

II
Crosby Beach yearns,
desiring feet, paws; hungriest sand
churning slithers of light.
They watch day shrink to a line
in always too much sky.
Rusted eyes sweep for news
know there is no use searching light
or the sea's dark knots; no use
fathoming for truth among the wafting roots
of something far more deeply interfused.

III
The estuary skims them –
wet, salted breeze, gull keens, a frigate's low horn
dimmed by white miles.
Light confuses sleek water
as tides change in their rusted minds.
A surge in the blood as they dream
their lost swelling on the horizon
slinks back, hope slumps
as they dread the ship sunk
whose dwelling is the light of setting suns.

IV

They have watched so long
time has mapped them with lurid crusts
frail rinds, oxide blisters.
Every day their grief brightens
as they let themselves rust

the bodies' changing tides laid bare
as they hold the water's stare
sift along the seam of last light
infusing their gaze with a final flare
and the round ocean and the living air.

V

They watch the beach forget.
The lost survive in corroding chests
eyes so brittle they have begun to flake.
They trail the breeze through cupped hands
but there is no sign in the cycles that graze them
no hint in bristling dunes, the deep suck of sand.
On the horizon, final fusion of sea and sun
snuffed, leaves their fissured stares, their blazing rusts.
No sign in blinking cities, swathes of farmland
and the blue sky, and in the mind of man.

After the sculpture 'Another Place'
by Anthony Gormley

115

Mother Fish
Ian Macartney

Mother Fish,
from which all life sits in its cerulean womb,
clicked alien tongues against the bank, percussive;
            each outward
gulp shot moons to the shore.
Clotted air – bubbles sketched
intricate veins behind the waves,
                    ashen valves,
      the thread from kelp's absence.
    Think the fronds of jellyfish, this
      the body of a jellyfish
      nestled as anti-peninsula
between the land's crab-hand,
the encrusted jewels of heather
            and me
Going back to the divide
            Again
Uncertain of all this giving
            Jumping freely
over stones
            The teeth of the beach

Woman from North India on Bostadh Beach
Elinor Brooks

She'd come on holiday with friends from Inverness
selling jewellery, 'high quality' necklaces
made by girls from Thailand and Nepal
to tempt the tourists at the summer stalls.

Her kids jumped in the waves, shrieked at the cold –
close by us lay an urchin, a gull-white bowl
pricked out in dainty needlepoint and packed with sand.
The woman's swollen belly would not let her bend

and so I gathered for her unborn baby's hands
shells and pebbles, tiny coral fronds.
The surging sea, indifferent, still rolled
its treasures round each continent and pole:

together we stood and watched the rising swell
that at full height would ring the Time-tide bell.

Points of Interest
Olivia Dawson

Every morning I open my front door and step out
into a stuccoed world. There are unstolen
bottles of milk standing like skittles on the porch,

no moody cloud forests or brilliant salt flats
just a hopscotch of concrete that leads to school,
the High Street, the forbidden fruits of Biba.

At home my father helps me trace maps of Bolivia,
we mark Grandmother's grave in La Paz with a cross,
track the vagaries of the Rio Magdalena to find
Great Grandpa's house in Mompox. Weighted

with an unpronounceable name on my satchel
I take care to speak English and hope
nobody clocks me. All I long for is to set sail
for places I know so well but have never known.

We Dig the Pig
Angel Warwick

In the hull of a silt-clad
oyster smack, we dig the pig
iron from beside the chine

and struggle – muddy,
to drag them back to bank
– Fat century-old swine.

Down the weigh-station
baffled in heave of the pickup
(greased metal pricks)

and hands fork cash for
river-black sleeper agents,
whose weight will aid the tick-

tick, when night tide consumes
the egret's patter spot
in a godly yawn.

Ovčice, Croatia
Ian Macartney

On this slim torso of a beautiful man
called Earth we slip palms
under beaches of coin,
eggshell smooth as china plate
beside a froth-cracked pool of melting jade
throwing mesh-net mountains
into the air, waves slapping their stars
on rock, glittering reflections preserved in salt...
this crystal oil smooths all brick.
In sea-reflected life we slip our palms
into scoops under big sand,
brief gods of trickling mini-mountains
under glancing sun.

When Will We See the Sea?
Joy Howard

Feeling we know you
we rush to your side
laden with sandwiches, flasks
swimsuits, towels.

With shouts of delight
or silent awe we greet you
immerse ourselves
in your amenable surf.

As with other friends
we learn that you have secrets,
sudden depths, no-go areas
changes of mood.

We want to trust you, but this
is all we really know:
your waves will go on breaking
when our tides have gone out.

I Nearly Drownded, Daddy
Vivien Jones

As a child, one of three, play-swimming
in the lacy-edged, turquoise, kind Mediterranean,
staying close to Daddy's strong arms,

in a moment of brash adventure, I dove
right under, eyes open in a sea of legs,
forgot to hold my breath, and breathed.

Daddy hoiked me up by my swimsuit straps,
a dripping dead weight, spluttering, coughing,
he slapped my back none too softly.

I nearly drownded, Daddy – I wept dramatically,
he laughed, he just laughed as if it was nothing,
carried me to shore over his uncaring shoulder.

*

I see the children's bodies, the ones who did drown,
in the cold, navy-blue, unkind Mediterranean.
they are layered on the sea's dark bottom,

still clutching likewise drowned parents,
flung over their shoulders, quietly embracing
siblings in a lacework of right-angled limbs.

On a Day Like This
Savanna J A Evans

She pressed every fingertip on her
last child's shoulder,
as her arms were the locket clasp
pinned to every youngers' napes,
the hand fell short not a day ago.

She stands with her other five,
water separates them
from her first
 — under churned soil.
So far from that place
they knew.

Decades from now
her children's grandchildren
will be told
they do not belong
on this land.

Delivery
Holly Blades

Labour was like this:
Rise up with the waves
in a warm ocean, before
the break   up up up down
up up up down   gentle lift
breathless moment
at the top
fall
sink
into hot
sand
collapse

Rise
again

I lay in a dark room
hooked to machines
let the waves lift me
It might have been midday
the glare white and merciless
up   up   up   down
It might have been Bermuda
up   up   up   down
I lost track of hours

When I was small I stayed
in the water all day
in New Jersey
diving under waves
to feel the whoosh over
my body, all that power

Hit it wrong and go tumbling
sand in your hair
ground face-first into rushing
foaming force
that could suck a child
down   I learned
respect

On the other side
of that same ocean
thirty years later
the end was like that:
caught in the breaking
crest   dragged under
landing roughly
and hurt   skin scraped off
a small surprised creature
crying beside me   sunburned
crusted
with dried white salt

'Don't scream, daughter,' the nurse said
languidly – to me, not the baby.
She spoke in Portuguese. I semi
understood; I shut up.
This was a new
place. Somehow
it was still night.
I prayed for morning
grateful for the wave
that took us to shore

First Light
Laura Potts

It is somewhere in a sometime
that a long late light
  on the other side of this city's eyes
holds the dark hills

and the voice of a mother
            is chiming
like goblets
  through the lobes
          of the trees

in that moment when she cradles
                    in the crick of her bone
the silver limbs
  the candled skin

and there are moons
which are trembling
and spin
  in the warm air

where the tiny light asleep
is her

                    moon man

her lamplight
shipwrecked
        at sea

and one day the soldier

  slumped to his
                knees.

Casting a Daughter Adrift
Emma Lee

Refugee camp, Lebanon

The earth tilts again and I stop.
Will I ever rid myself of these sea legs?
I swallow air without smelling.
My daughter found some petals
I crushed into perfume for her.
Today she should smell good.
I roll my feet and move to the rhythm
of my toothache. She danced off
first thing. Excitement caused
her insomnia. I doze in short bursts,
wary of strange men and foreign tongues.
During the light hours I sew
to earn, thinking I am at least
armed with needles and pins.
This man I have agreed to
in her father's absence
I hope will protect her.
I carried her at shoulder height
on the boat so she wasn't crushed.
The final payment is the last of my savings
but I have one less mouth to feed.
I have work waiting but today is hers.
The shop's cracked, foxed mirror
tells me I'm decades older than my bones.
This green dress is as dark
as the sea we floated and prayed on.
Her smile outshines her white, sequinned dress.
I'm going to let her go,
my desert flower will bloom
and I hope he remains kind
and maintains the protection
I can no longer give her.
The house she was born in is rubble,
her new home is sticks and tarpaulin.
But today is the wedding of her dreams.

Hawser
Sarah Tait

rope-caught
snake-chained
heave-stretch
twist-fight

pull

grimace-braced
breath-held
iron-clenched
curse-grunt

hold

salt-shore
callous-borne
leather-skinned
muscle-burned

moored

shanty-cord
taut-heft
breeze-taught
load-lowered

stowed

sail-reefed
coin-jinked
ale-brimmed
moon-cupped

dawn

mast-rigged
tide-trimmed
wheel-spun
wind-held

gone

Bosun's Locker
Sarah Tait

Lots of things would be better, I think,
than being slapped round the chops
with a wet fish,
the smell of fish-juice ice to run the chin,
the gape of gill and fixed-gasp fat-lip *oh*,
upon the slip-shine pile
to land the haddock thump.

And lots of things might be better, too,
than this empty quay,
the silence where shouts rung out,
and gasped the ice, not long ago.

A flounder for your thoughts
you cod-struck chap, you sea-bass lass,
will you take a whack
right round your boat?
No china here, just plaice and skate
just caught,
once caught,
the smell of fish-juice ice to linger, linger long
so long
not long ago, the fixed-gasp fat-lipped *oh* –

No Tearaways
Ivonne Piper

Son of a Greek
disobeyed his father
flew too high
got burnt by the sun
fell into the ocean

but not you my boy
I'm your mother
not if I have my say
in the matter
no tearaways here oh no

and I said
        and I said as you do
but they grow
            and GROW don't they
then they go their ways
wine and song etcetera
all that

So now I know
he won't come home
on water-skis or whatever
trolling the paths
of those wild seas

he is pleased to skid over
and along
as if
as if...

Sea Lessons
Ness Owen

She tells you everyone
born by sea is brave.
Like the cockle women
you must live by tides,
chasing the ebb, waiting
for the turn. There's little
time between high and
low, but the oystercatcher
knows to swoop at her
chance. She tells you
no one can outrun her,
only count for the ninth
wave that'll carry you to
shore. Like the marram grass
weavers, bend, fold over and
under from mother to daughter
pass on all that you learn.

City of Water
JN nucifera

I have always sailed on easterly winds
pushing my ship toward twilight
racing towards a longer day
if only for a second more,

but here,
the canals flow out
into the cradle of history,
fertilising art with salt:
seasoning it, preserving it.

History has turned blind in the eastern winds –
too strange, too foreign,
as though all that can be seen
is a hello from due east,
a nihao from the sunrise.

I have tried to race towards sunset,
to see what kind of blindness
might exist in the night

here,
I docked my ship, lost myself in the
winding water-lined streets,
stood still where the wind blows
into reflections of homes,
parting facades with force,
unveiling it, eroding it

when you season anything with the Aegean,
it is bound to taste unfamiliar in my mouth,
but there will always be traces
of the sands from the Gebi in the floral patterns
just beneath.

A shame that the desert
means death,
not nourishment for a longer life.

So I continue my path west
turning blind myself, with the salt in my eyes
as I carry the desert sands with me in the wind.

Crossing the Black Water
Reshma Ruia

My son he crossed the black water
Ate beef and woke each morning
To the razor cut breath of cold
I heard him calling me in my sleep
So, my sari wrapped tight around my hips
I too leapt across the black waters
It was hard at first
The language like an alphabet soup
Bubbling inside my mouth
The grey days that shut me in like a wall
But by God I learnt damn fast
Stopped waiting for the street vendor's call
To haggle over onions and potatoes in the bazaar
To leave my gold bangles behind when I caught
 The 151 bus to Asda each week
I don't go on the roof anymore
To spot the moon of *karva-chauth*
The landlord filed a complaint
I've learnt to love the rain that falls
Feeble and timid upon my skin
I've learnt to forget
The bare-breast joy of the monsoon at home
Diwali comes and goes but I see no little boys lighting crackers on the
 streets
Never mind I will make some pudding with condensed milk
The English are organised and most up to date
My son reminds me everyday
No dripping roof or tap
No wild flower or tree
No unnecessary smiles or hugs
Everything trimmed. To the point
What's not to love?

He gets up for work
As the world shuts its eye
A graduate at home he drives lorries for a living
Scowls anger when I watch my Indian TV
Watch BBC. Learn English he says
No need I reply with a shrug
It's time I found a wife for my son
A girl from back home
With cheeks plump and skin so fair
Together we will sit and watch Zee TV
And chat about how good life was
On the other side of the black water

Crossing the ocean – kalapan or black water – was a
huge taboo among orthodox Hindus in Colonial India,
as it signified losing one's heritage and values.

Tulpaner och Liljekonvaljer
Carl Alexandersson

The tulips made me think of you
I told her that you were
Cremated, and that we buried
Your urn
She told me that she'd prefer
For her ashes to be scattered
To the ocean
And to have a bench dedicated to her
That people could sit on in the wind
In sunsets and sunrises
Sharing time
With others and the world

I never think about death
I guess death for me is about
Endings, finality
Maybe it isn't

The little kid runs along the beach
Flying his kite
It's red, and blue, yellow, and green
And he's proud to fly it
The other kids dig holes in the sand with shovels
And pretend to bury one
A few people are kayaking, calmly
And the rest of us just look
She's an ocean spirit
She wants to take part in it all
She removes her shoes
And waits for me to do the same

Today I learned
That your second favourite flower
Is called 'lily of the valley'
In English
I like to think that you help
The earth
Grow them
The lilies and the tulips both

The bench we're sitting on
She and I
Is dedicated to a woman named Lily
Who we never knew
Yet the world keeps moving
She moves towards the water
And I imagine your flowers swaying in the wind
As I remove my shoes.

Paddling
Lynn White

No one swam in the seas round Britain
when I was a child.
The water was empty beyond the edge
of the shore
even on the warmest of days.
Paddling was as adventurous as it got.
Nothing wetter was allowed,
Trousers rolled up,
skirts tucked in knickers
clothes to be protected from
the saltwater waves.
Only then was paddling allowed
taking due care not to kick or jump,
taking due care not to let the wet waves
go too far.

TIDE

FILM-POEM

TEXTS

Open Water
Susan Cartwright-Smith

We are all shapes and sizes. Scars criss-cross our bodies: operations, childbirth, weight loss, weight gain. The folds of our maps are deep and ingrained. Our contours contain our stories, some chapters missing, some yet to be written.

The water is different each time. The feeling in the air, the frost, the mist. Each time there is a new experience, even from the same point of entry. The environment offers up its challenges, its possibilities. We have to decide if we accept the challenge today. We usually do.

So too is our internal landscape different. To each other and each time. Our personal tides, our ebbs, our flows. Mentally and physically. Each time is a catharsis, a baptism, a cleansing of the soul. We enter the water rubbed out and meditative. We have to be, for we must listen to ourselves at these temperatures. We must concentrate on every twinge, every ache, every scream of the blood. The cold makes narcissists of us all, but our reflections are not for others to gaze upon; our reflections are within, during these cold months.

We each have a shadow of darkness about us – for the most we are ebullient, but some days are carved, and that is when the hive draws close and we need the freshness of surgical sharp water to slice through the grey curtain.

Some days the earth is breathing out: swirling mists roiling, smudging the water colour landscape, as we descend to the water's edge. Sometimes the water is warmer than the air outside, despite our shrieks, as we strip and plunge. The bee stings of snowflakes, the heavy pad of raindrops, and the blinding surprise of sunrise peering over the mountain tops. We can never predict what our heads will encounter as our bodies are submerged.

The bone-deadening numbness. The dagger-sharp shooting. The prickle of white-hot coldness. All the different sensations alive, alert. The pain that wakens us to feeling. And we return for more.

The shivering and the aftershocks are part of our recovery and experience. Acute. Great hunger. Waves of exhaustion. All appetites on edge. And throughout it all is a great happiness. Camaraderie, conversations. We compare equipment, we offer technique ideas, we swap recipes, talk trash, laugh. We laugh. So much. We feel happy, without feeling guilty. At least for the time we are there. This pleasure is ours. Not to enhance anyone else's life, for that brief time, as mothers, wives, workers – demands of us are put aside, and we listen to ourselves, look within.

In the cold, we swim quickly, submerge swiftly. We want the experience to last, but know it cannot. The warmer months offer the choice to swim alongside each other and chat, but these bitter days see us strike out alone with our thoughts. The mountains cradle us, and the vastness of the sky and lake focus us into this speck; we are small, and a part of the landscape. This is different to the controllable numbered laps of an indoor pool. This is swimming to lose yourself in, and swimming to find yourself in. We are vulnerable, but we wear our battle scars internally and externally and re-enter the womb of the world.

We accept the challenge and for a short while know freedom.

Modality
Julie Laing

KEYNOTE   Overarching wind
              drops
              the corpse of hearing.
              Lull.
              M8 six miles distant, earbeat close
              persists,
              has not stopped is borne
              under over above
              fields river air ear, is lifted
              by the
              overarching
              wind.

SOUNDMARK Civic chime quavers over
                        SITE FOR REDEVELOPMENT,
              reduced by phone clocks and earphones.

              Oh Lord our God thy children call
              does not appeal to
              students
              unhearing,
              landscape
              undocked. It is

SIGNAL   bound by everhum of engines.   *KL1477*
              In overalls they smack a breaktime ball   *from Amsterdam*
              around the turning   *trails*
              point, beaten by the gust which tugs   *reverb*
              through the landscaped limes, and laughter,   *boulders*
              to anechoic wasteland   *to*
              and snuffs between campus and clock tower   *diminuendo*
              beyond   *beyond*
              the river   *the river*
                slap slap slipslap slap slipslaps lap slaplap sliplap lipslaps

UNSIGNAL   unbanter
             uncurse
             unlaugh
             unfouroclockhomehorn
             unhammer
             unrivet
             unweld
             unwishthisshipandallwhosailinher

             underneath
             the pterodactyl crane

             there is
             peace

About the authors

There isn't room here to tell you all about the authors, but each of them has a page on our website where you can find out about their strange hobbies and other publications. https://arachnepress.com/writers

About Arachne Press

Arachne Press is a micro publisher of (award-winning!) short story and poetry anthologies and collections, novels including a Carnegie Medal nominated young adult novel, and a photographic portrait collection.
We are expanding our range all the time, but the short form is our first love. We keep fiction and poetry live, through readings, festivals (in particular our Solstice Shorts Festival), workshops, exhibitions and all things to do with writing. https://arachnepress.com/

Follow us on Twitter:
@ArachnePress
@SolShorts

Like us on Facebook:
ArachnePress
SolsticeShorts2014